The Valley of Rubies

Also by Joseph Kessel

THE LION

JOSEPH KESSEL

The Valley of Rubies

Translated from the French by
STELLA RODWAY

DAVID McKAY COMPANY, INC.

New York

To Jean Rosenthal

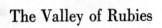

The Valley of Rubies

1

I T W A S a Sunday in autumn. It had been drizzling all morning, and the Paris sky seemed to be pressing down upon the glistening slate of the roof-tops.

I was alone, savouring the delights of doing nothing. Having only just come back from a long, torrid voyage, I felt refreshed by the coolness and the dark pearly grey of the rain. I was thinking of finding a mild and fertile spot in the heart of the country where I could bury myself, recover my equilibrium, and start some plodding work on one of the books that had been in my mind for so long.

My dreams were interrupted by the harsh unwelcome sound of the doorbell. I wasn't expecting anyone, so I didn't get up. But the noise became louder and louder, more and more penetrating. I knew I should have to answer it, but I cursed the intruder.

Yet when I looked out on the landing and met the gaze of a pair of brilliant blue eyes, set in a pointed, freckled face, all my anger evaporated.

Some people have the power to disarm you whatever they do, and my friend Jean belongs to this race of beings. He is domineering, but always exquisitely kind. He is excitable, highly volatile, and utterly ingenuous and sincere. He is absurdly generous, but shamefaced about it. He is also crazy, though in a way that has all the attributes of logic.

Jean never comes into a room: he bursts in. He never walks: he runs. He never speaks, he is seized by sudden bouts of fever. He has no ordinary, balanced, commonplace feelings, only transports of enthusiasm. He is perpetually on fire.

During the war he brought this spirit to his work with the Maquis in Savoy, coming and going between London and France, dropping by parachute or landing by plane, and carrying out the most dangerous missions, always with the same joyful, unconscious heroism.

He has now resumed his peace-time occupation, which is the buying and selling of precious stones. This, too, is performed with characteristic abandon.

It is scarcely surprising that a person so much in love with life should be loved by life in return.

Jean charged right into my flat.

'I hope I'm not disturbing you——' he cried, giving me no chance to reply. 'Have you got any plans on at the moment?'

I started to tell him about my idea of finding a retreat, so that I could get on with my work.

'That's fine!' he broke in, enthusiastically. 'A jolly good idea.'

It was clear that he wasn't paying the least attention to what he was saying. I had the impression that he was waiting for something.

Then the doorbell rang again.

'Ah, that'll be Julius,' said Jean. 'He's a colleague of mine. I arranged to meet him here. You'll like him—he's a funny chap.'

With that he rushed towards the hall.

The 'funny chap' was a short, stocky man of about sixty, with a swarthy skin and a square head, on which his close-cropped grey hair curled like astrakhan. His wide mouth wore an expression of great caution, and the look in his eye was reserved. He talked in English, speaking it well, but sparingly, and with an odd, Oriental accent.

'I want to show you something Julius has brought back from London,' said Jean.

The man with the astrakhan hair mechanically wiped his glasses, which had thick horn rims. Then he felt in his waistcoat pocket and drew out a tiny packet wrapped in tissue paper. Jean unwrapped it neatly and with tender care. A red stone sparkled in his palm. 'Just have a look at that,' he said. He spoke in the passionate voice of a lover. 'Just look at it. It's a very rare jewel: a twenty-carat ruby, perfectly cut.'

Julius came closer. His wide face had lost a little of its Buddhist serenity.

'Pigeon's blood,' he said. 'As pure a stone as you could see . . .'

I didn't understand their jargon, but even through the gloom of that rainy day I could perceive clearly enough the translucent fire which smouldered with such miraculous intensity inside the crimson scrap of light.

'How much have we refused for this?' asked Jean.

'Forty-five million francs,' replied his colleague, wiping his glasses.

'Take it for a moment and hold it against your face,' said Jean to me, his loving gaze still fixed upon the jewel. 'It's warm. You can feel the life in it.'

But the moment it was between my fingers he let out a cry.

'Look out, you're going to drop it. It's fragile, you know. You'll break it.'

I was shocked. 'Do you mean to tell me that this costs over forty-five million francs and that it'll break? For heaven's sake take it away again.'

Once again the stone rested on Jean's palm. I gazed upon this incredible fortune that took up so little room.

'This is what you find in Mogok,' said Jean quietly.

'Mogok? Where's that?'

The face which Julius turned to me was incredulous, even stern.

'Mogok!' he replied. 'Why, it's in Burma, of course—Upper Burma.'

Jean laughed, the freckles dancing round his blue eyes.

'You can see why Julius is surprised,' he said. 'He's been travelling to and from Mogok since 1920, and since the end of the war he's spent more than eight months a year there.'

Julius, upon whose features sat the limitless patience of the East, gave a sigh.

'Nice and cool,' was all he said. It was his favourite phrase.

Then the pair of them began to tell me about Mogok. Jean's voice, ardent as ever, rose and fell, while Julius talked in more sober strain.

'The valley of Mogok,' they said, 'lies in the north of Burma, far beyond Mandalay, between high jungle-covered hills. There have been rubies there since the beginning of time. Wrapped in their coating of rough mineral, they have lain hidden in the bowels of the rocks, along the streams, deep in the mountain-sides. There—and nowhere else.

'For, as far as the memory of mankind goes back, no one has ever discovered another part of the earth's crust that will yield stones such as these—as bright as flame, as red as blood.

'Rubies are mentioned in some of the earliest writings that exist: in the Koran, in the Song of Songs, in the ancient records of India and China. Since time immemorial they have shone in the crowns and diadems of princes, kings and emperors, or lain hidden in the treasure-houses of the rajahs. Every one of them, from the most recently discovered to the oldest of all, must have come from Mogok.

'In those dim, distant times, who can have mined them, sold them, and carried them away from this wild and desolate country? No one knows: it remains a total mystery. There are magnificent legends about Mogok, but no actual records. Our knowledge of its history goes back only four hundred years.

'Yet the fact remains that, as far as it is humanly possible to discover, there can be no other geological origin for the rubies of legend and history: they must have been formed in the rocks of Mogok. And it is still this valley which supplies the world with those flame-bright, blood-red stones whose facets sparkle in the jewellers' shops of the great capitals.'

All the time Jean and Julius were telling me these things, flashes as from a red star were shining through the grey Paris light from the twenty-carat ruby—the ruby from Mogok.

At length Julius picked it up, gazed at it for a moment, and sighed.

'You don't find many like this,' he said, 'even there.'

He wrapped the ruby carefully in tissue paper again and slipped the packet back into his waistcoat pocket.

'All the finest stock has completely disappeared,' he complained. 'It's just like a bad dream.'

He began to wipe his glasses briskly. I realized that this was a nervous habit, by which he soothed himself when he was excited.

'We've talked so much shop,' he said to Jean, 'that I haven't had a chance to tell you about this incredible business.'

He put his glasses back on again and paused to make sure that we were listening. Then he slowly told his story.

'This tale,' said he, 'goes back about thirty years, to the time when the most famous dacoit—the fiercest highway robber in the whole of the Mogok area—decided that he had had enough of the dangers and difficulties of his profession. He paid a sort of tax to the police in order to make 'sure that he would be treated as a respectable citizen, and then he set himself up in the jewel trade, both as a dealer and a mine-owner. He had quite a bit of capital, as you can imagine. Then—I don't know why—it may have been his flair, or good luck, or by intimidating his competitors—or even through invoking the spirits, as they think over there—but somehow all the finest sapphires and rubies managed to come his way. There were some truly remarkable pieces among them, but he never sold them. He kept them for himself.'

Julius broke off and removed his glasses.

Without them his face was more exposed, and more ingenuous-looking than usual, which emphasized the expression of reverent inner contemplation that appeared upon it at that moment.

'What a collection!' he said. 'It was no ordinary dealer's hoard—it was fit for a prince, or a museum. I often used to go and look at it. And then, last year, the old bandit died. Some weird illness or other. They say his daughter was an expert on herbs—beneficial and otherwise. Anyway, the daughter and her husband left and took a house at Tchaipine, which is the other ruby centre in the Mogok valley. No doubt they hoped to be forgotten. But one night there was an attack on the house and it was set on fire. The daughter and her husband were burnt with it. All the wonderful stones vanished without trace. None of the dealers, nor their agents, has seen a sign of them anywhere. And it was a museum collection—a king's treasure!'

'Do you hear that?' cried Jean. 'What a story! Isn't it wonderful!'

He rushed on without a pause.

'I've never been to Mogok. It's criminal. Julius is going back there in three days' time. I've decided to join him as soon as possible. Are you coming?'

For a moment dreams of peace and work flitted back into my conscience. Should I go, just one more trip . . .

'We could call at Bombay and Calcutta,' Jean was saying. 'I've got people I could see there. Then Rangoon. From there there's a Dakota which does the trip to Upper Burma once a week . . .'

'When do we leave?' I asked.

There was a sound rather like a groan.

'Not so fast. Not so fast . . .' said Julius. He was wiping his glasses feverishly. 'You do want to think it over carefully.

Living conditions out there are worse than primitive. And the Mogok area is very far from safe. It's infested with rebels and bandits. Travellers are being attacked all the time.'

Jean laughed with all his freckles. He was only too well aware of what it was like when I heard the call of adventure.

'We can leave as soon as Julius gives us the green light from Mogok,' he said.

'Nice and cool,' sighed Julius.

* * *

One of the wonderful things about going on a long journey is the way the magic begins before you actually set out—when you open the atlas and begin to dream over the maps, rolling round your tongue the splendid names of towns you've never been to.

I often did this after that day when Jean had decided for me that I was to go to Mogok with him. In fact I had already ceased to belong properly to my ordinary surroundings. As I went about my daily round I found myself looking beyond familiar things and familiar faces at glimpses in my mind's eye of tropical trees and flowers, of gleaming seas, of bronzed skins, and high Mongol cheek-bones.

* * *

Julius was now back in Mogok. We had only to wait for the agreed signal before setting out.

A week passed. Then another. Then several more. No signal came. Gradually my impatience grew. Soon I was angry.

Jean had to put up with my moods, since it was all his own doing. He bore them with surprising fortitude, especially as he is normally far and away the more excitable of us two. But his profession, like every other, has its own discipline.

'You must understand,' he would say, 'that it's entirely up to Julius. It's for him to decide. My own knowledge of the East doesn't go any further than India. I've never been to Mogok, whereas Julius, as you know, has been visiting the country for the last thirty years, and has lived there ever since the end of the war. He speaks Hindustani and Burmese as fluently as English. He's got his finger on the pulse of the people out there: he knows exactly how to handle them and how to discover what's going on. He has his own methods of locating stock, of assessing the conditions, and everything.'

'What a lot of fuss about buying a few stones!'

'But these stones are among the rarest in the world,' said Jean, seriously. 'They have a way of hiding, and of disappearing altogether. And on the spot, watching out for them all the while, there's a whole community of wily dealers, with their agents, their informers, their spies.'

'I should have thought you could have seen better for yourself.'

'I can't travel like a tourist,' said Jean. 'Nor even like a writer. I can't afford the luxury of serving an apprenticeship in Mogok. For one thing, I haven't the time. But a more important reason is that I should lose face with the people there. It's much better for Julius to do the spade-work in advance, so that I can arrive at the end, when everything is ready, and pull off a big *coup*. Otherwise I might have to spend months there. You've no idea what bargaining is like in the East.'

These conversations usually took place in Jean's office in the rue Lafayette. The business where he worked had been founded by his father many years ago. A bearded fellow, who looked like a genial ogre, Jean's father had come over from the Caucasus at the end of the last century without a penny to his name, and had built up a vast empire in the pearl business. Then, when the Japanese pearls ruined him completely, he went off to America and made his fortune again, at the age of eighty.

Now, Jean shares the offices with his uncle, another character who has gone down to legend for exploits in a more heroic age, when he rode through Arabia on horseback, travelled off the islands of the Persian Gulf in a *sambouk*, and lived in India like a rajah.

The entrance to the offices was barred with a steel grille, like a bank strong-room, and the guard let no one through unless he knew them. Even so, Jean's two rooms swarmed all day long with people of a race apart: buyers, merchants, and agents of both sexes.

Their deals involved a whole paraphernalia of magnifying glasses, little balances of dead accuracy, with tiny weights, and very fine tongs. The precision of their movements and the extreme delicacy of the instruments brought home to me how, in that business, every milligram counted, every slight gradation in colour, every subtle reflection of light.

But the market value was clearly not all that mattered to these people. When a stone of real quality appeared, their faces would light up with an admiration that was quite disinterested. The stones had a mystique for them, a poetry.

Jean would talk about his work with passionate enthusiasm.

'You see,' he explained, 'how many factors are brought into play. First there's the weight—the number of carats. Then there's the cutting—the workmanship. And then the colour. Lastly, there's the brilliance and transparency—the way the light acts upon it. The variations in all these things can mean that two stones of the same weight may be vastly different in value. You'll often get a ten-carat stone that's worth much more than one of twenty carats. Look at this . . .'

There might be an emerald sparkling at the end of his tongs, or a sapphire. Sometimes it would be a diamond or a ruby. . . .

'Jewels have always been desired and sought after,' he said, 'ever since man first began to live in communities. It's a taste which goes back thousands of years. And men have learnt to pay dearly for these objects of their love. Precious stones have come actually to represent wealth—wealth, what's more, in the form which is least in volume, and most easily handled, carried about, and hidden. That's very important, especially nowadays when wars and crises and migrations have become a part of everyday life.'

As part of my education in this field of which I knew nothing, Jean taught me the hierarchy of jewels, with the blue sapphire first, the green emerald next, leading up to the red ruby at the top—the ruby of Mogok.

Then my impatience would break out again, and Jean would have to say once more, 'But we must wait for news from Julius.'

At last a telegram arrived.

I was in Jean's office when his secretary brought it in to him. I could tell from the way he opened it that his own excitement was as intense as mine. But instead of reading it straight away he took a thick book that looked like a dictionary from his desk and began to riffle through it.

'What on earth are you doing?' I almost wailed.

'I'm decoding the telegram,' he said, as though this was the most ordinary thing in the world.

He raised his freckled face to mine for a moment and saw how surprised I was.

'Where such things as prices are concerned,' he said, 'post offices aren't a bit confidential. Particularly in small towns in the Far East.'

He was silent again as he bent over the dictionary and transcribed a few words.

'I don't believe in letting our competitors in Mogok know what we're up to,' he continued. 'Nor does Julius. All about our purchases, what we're paying, what our plans are, what information we've got . . .'

Jean's eyes, very blue behind his spectacles, were brighter than usual.

'This job, though it involves other things, of course, is a bit like the secret service. A good piece of confidential information can be worth a fortune. I remember once some information I had about an Empress's jewellery—a wonderful set of jewels which was closely involved with the history of France, about a hundred years ago. Her heirs had just brought it right across Europe by the most romantic means, in order to get it to a northern capital.'

'What Empress?' I wanted to know. 'What means? What capital?'

'I'm not allowed to tell you,' said Jean. 'We all have our professional secrets.'

For a few moments he riffled his book in silence, wrote something down, then riffled again. Then he put the book back in its usual place.

He had apparently finished the decoding.

'Well,' I said, 'when do we leave?'

Jean made no reply. Instead he showed me his transcription.

'Journey most inadvisable stop,' I read. *'No interesting stone in view stop District increasingly dangerous Julius.'*

I dropped the piece of paper and looked across at Jean. He shrugged his shoulders, embarrassed.

'I'll send Julius a cable,' he said.

'What will you say?'

'I'll ask him to send us news regularly.'

After that, Julius cabled every week to say that, from a professional point of view, it was useless to go to Mogok. Also, the situation was growing increasingly dangerous. Reading between the lines, I could see that the very idea of our making the journey was an anathema to him.

I began to lose hope.

Then, one morning, Jean came to see me, bursting into my flat in his usual fashion. From the gleam in his eye, and from the general liveliness of features and freckles, I gathered, without his having to tell me, that we were to be off at last.

'Does this mean a favourable wire from Julius?' I cried. 'In spite of everything?'

'No, it isn't that,' said Jean.

'What is it then?'

We were alone in the room. Yet instinctively Jean gave a rapid glance round, and lowered his voice.

'Do you remember the story Julius told us that Sunday when I brought him here?' he asked. 'About the old highway robber—the former dacoit—who became a ruby king in Mogok? And about the suspicious circumstances of his death? And how his fabulous collection of jewels was stolen, and nobody has heard a word of it since? A museum collection, Julius called it—and he ought to know. Do you remember?'

As if I would have forgotten! The story had weighed considerably in my decision to go to Mogok.

Jean lowered his voice again, till he was whispering.

'Well,' he said, 'I've had some news . . .'

'From Julius?'

'No, not from him,' he said, more loudly. 'But don't ask me anything about that. I've already told you—we never disclose our sources of information.'

He leant towards me and whispered again.

'Apparently someone has got on the track of the stones—or some of them—from the old bandit's hoard.'

There was dead silence in the room. Then it was shattered by a burst of delighted laughter.

'It'll be more wonderful than ever to go for a reason like this,' he cried. 'Don't you think so?'

THE aeroplane that was to take us to Bombay came via London and landed at Orly. It was a Constellation, like a great many others—but, unlike them, it was called the *Himalayan Princess*, and it belonged to Air India.

I must admit that this made me feel a little uneasy. Over the years, I had travelled on long flights only by European or American lines. They were known, wealthy, and long enough established to be seasoned, with their own traditions. When you're being taken to a distant part of the world, at considerable altitude, over water, desert and mountain, it's pleasant to feel that you're in familiar hands. Yet here I was, entrusting myself to a plane belonging to an exotic company, with the crew walking towards it at that moment—a crew whose dark skins and huge gleaming eyes belonged to other suns and skies than mine.

I looked at Jean. He was stroking (rather nervously, I thought) the green plumes in the striped turban of a red doll, in the form of a rajah. It was the Company's emblem, which he had stolen from the Air India office. I thought I could detect in his movements, if not actual anxiety, at least the feeling that he needed a mascot. I looked away from him, and went towards the *Himalayan Princess*.

But if ever fears were ill-founded, mine were. Our journey took us as far as Hong-Kong, and back to Paris again, and for the whole of it not only were we as safe as with any of the best or oldest air lines, but our comfort was attended to with the most remarkable care. There was the same efficiency at the airports as when we were in full flight.

It is true, of course, that Air India cover only one route, and can give all their attention to it. It is also true that the company is better equipped than any other to serve this route, having a closer knowledge and understanding of the language and customs of the country. It is a young company, and there is therefore a more dynamic spirit among its personnel. Though it is nationalized, it still derives a certain impulse from its founder, who was a great captain of industry.

All the same, when disaster befell me and I lost my passport at Calcutta there was no obligation on a young officer of Air India to go rushing through the overpowering heat to the photographers, police stations and consulates in order to fetch me all the necessary permits, visas and forms for my journey within a few hours. It was a most extraordinary feat.

However, when the *Himalayan Princess* began to steer towards the East, I knew nothing of all this. But I was already under a spell.

Usually, an aeroplane journey is so swift that it precludes those gradual sensations of being taken out of your surroundings, that gentle ripening of the voyage that come with a sea-trip. New countries don't slowly come towards you—you're shot towards them. But on the *Himalayan Princess*, because of the nationality of the plane and of the personnel, there was something more natural about the transition from one world to another. The air hostess's musical voice, her calm dignity and grace; the steward's fine muscular back under his white shirt; the face of the pilot, an Indian who had served in the R.A.F., even the food—these things helped to mitigate the shock of a sudden change. They were a preparation for India—they spoke of her.

The final touch to the unusual atmosphere was added at Cairo, where we landed during the night. An elderly man boarded the plane. He was tall and upright of carriage, dressed in white, and with an aristocratic face. His only retinue consisted of a secretary and two elderly women, in saris, and of very dignified bearing. Though the head of a great people—and one of the three or four world leaders—Pandit Nehru travelled for this twelve-hour stretch under the same conditions as all the other passengers.

I watched him closely during the journey. Throughout—when the plane soared over the dark Arabian deserts, streaked by pipe-lines, fanning out like flames, or when, in broad daylight, it glided over the Indian Ocean—Nehru kept his eyes closed and his face quite still. Was he sleeping, merely resting, or dreaming? I wondered. Or did the power of thought enable him to achieve spiritual union with the universe? This was the man who had come from British colonial prisons to be one of the arbiters of the British Empire. Nourished upon a philosophy which is among the oldest, the most contemplative, and the most opposed to movement, he was now engaged in leaping from continent to continent.

At Santa Cruz, the aerodrome at Bombay, a team came on board and sprayed the whole aeroplane with insecticide. For five minutes no one was allowed to leave the plane, which was like an oven from the fierce heat of the sun, to say nothing of the stench. Pandit Nehru waited with the rest.

When he eventually left, he was surrounded by a crowd which hid him from our view.

Also, an old Hindu was coming towards Jean, with expansive gestures of welcome. He was followed by servants, carrying enormous garlands of jasmine, which they put round our necks. I felt somewhat embarrassed, but no one seemed to be paying any attention. The old man put his hands together on his chest and then raised them to his brow. Jean copied the gesture, then he turned to me.

'Allow me to introduce you to the oldest brother of one of the greatest jewellers in India. He heard news of our arrival and has come to offer us the customary welcome.'

A magnificent American car was waiting for us in front of the aerodrome. It carried us off to Bombay, along with our luggage and our fragrant garlands.

Bombay, say some, is the threshold of India.

Bombay, say others, has no connection with India at all.

Who cares? Bombay is a marvellous town, shapeless and endless, where the sea sparkles, the sun beats down, the colours clash; where, in a magnificent, dense, terrifying mass, crowds of Indians swarm, swarm, swarm, inexorably, inexhaustibly, in their flowing robes, in ascetic nakedness, in astrakhan hats, in luxurious turbans, in filthy rags, their clothes garish, their eyes dark and fiery, the marks of their religion upon their brows; where, facing the Taj Mahal Hotel, a city within the city, stands a triumphal arch called the Gateway to India, under which the Viceroy used to pass when he came to take up his post, and under which marched the British troops when the King of England gave up the finest crown in his Empire.

Bombay is a town where the public buildings are all like palaces and cathedrals, where, in the huge stations, in the parks, in the streets, sleep hundreds and thousands of men who have no other home, and never will have; where the factories smoke, where the rickshaws jog along, where brilliant flowers bloom; where the squares, the markets, the bazaars, the alleyways, the streets, and the temples teem endlessly and for ever; where, beneath soft, ethereal lights, coming from within, at the doors and windows of fragile, open, seemingly transparent houses, stand throughout the night thousands of women, like delicate, unreal statues, ghosts of blue, and mauve, and pink; where the biggest vultures in the world wheel incessantly in the darkening sky. Near the Tower of Silence, the Parsee tomb, where these carrion birds feed on the corpses, they can be seen crouching, in great filthy clusters, all over the branches of the trees.

Amid this chaos, this great boiling cauldron of riff-raff and magnificence, I went from jewel to jewel, from treasure to treasure. For my friend Jean, on his way to Mogok, would not have stopped in Bombay, however briefly, had it not been for his work.

First came the kingdom of pearls.

I entered it unwittingly by the back door one morning.

The sun was not yet very high over Bombay, but already the humidity was almost unbearable. The heat clung to one's skin like hot damp cloth. Our car could only crawl, for it had to penetrate a continually moving human dough, which glued up the narrow streets in this densely populated quarter, where the din was so loud that it drowned the blaring notes of the hooter, which our driver sounded at every second.

Jean, who knew and deeply loved the great towns of India, leant out over the crowd, breathing in its smells and smiling, as if unaware of what he was doing. He repeated to himself his favourite expression: 'Isn't it wonderful!'

He had the car parked in front of a tall, dingy house, against which surged this tumult of bodies and eager faces. A relative of his, who had settled in India forty years ago, had offices in this house.

'He has a sort of workshop, too,' Jean added. 'I'll leave a message for him with the foreman. The only thing is that we've got to go up five flights—but you can stop on the landing if you like. It's the same everywhere . . .'

It was indeed.

There was a stiff iron staircase, like a ladder, its steps reaching the roof of the building, on to which all the doors were open in order to draw some cool air into the rooms. It was like seeing a vast honeycomb in action. From the ground floor to the top it was composed of identical workshops, long, low rooms giving out on to the road. And in these workshops, hundreds of brown bodies, bony and gleaming with sweat, were bending over, squatted on their heels, between the workbenches. Each of the workmen held a sort of little bow, to the middle of which was fixed a very fine needle. The men, with neat, gentle, seeming perpetual movements, drew the thread of the bow so that the needle turned and turned continually. Under the point, held in a miniature vice, a pearl was fixed. Rotating invisibly because of their speed, a thousand needles entered at the same time into the milky substance, carving a very fine channel.

Through the thick crowd on the other side of the road I noticed an old temple. From time to time one of the pearl-piercers would straighten his damp neck and throw a glance—vacant or thoughtful—at the multi-coloured tiles, the ornate altars, the ancient gods, and the faithful prostrate before them, at the beggars with their sores, and at the children, unbearably beautiful in their filthy verminous rags, raising their little hands in supplication. The work would not cease, however. The string of the bow would continue to make the needle turn, and the pearls, pierced from one end to the other, would pile up in the workshops.

I asked Jean whether there was a demand for such quantities.

'Come and look,' he said.

The bazaar was a turmoil of noise and colour. We went among bales of woven and embroidered silk, of brilliant cottons, among fragrant wood and flowering shrubs, among figures which, for centuries and centuries, had represented gods and goddesses. And the whole bazaar, with its merchants, its stalls, its arcades and passages was submerged, as everywhere always was in Bombay, under a limitless, swelling, motley, turbulent crowd, where poverty and nakedness rubbed shoulders with wealth and luxury.

I looked around, dazzled.

'No,' said Jean, 'look over there.'

He pointed towards the outskirts of the bazaar. Here several plump, serious-looking men were moving backwards and forwards in the confined space at the edge of the road. There were at least twenty of them, and each had in his hand a large fly-whisk with a great bunch of very long thongs at the end. At first I couldn't understand why Jean had drawn my attention to these apparent idlers. But when I looked more closely at what they were holding I saw that the thongs of the fly-whisks were entirely composed of little oval balls, strung closely together, and giving out a strangely milky light.

They were pearls, and these men were pearl sellers.

At regular intervals they would tempt the passers-by, who elbowed and jostled their treasures, by carefully shaking the ends of the fly-whisks, making the pearl-encrusted thongs sing a soft music.

'It can't be true!' I said. 'They're imitation!'

'They're real all right,' said Jean.

'But they must be worth millions of——'

'Rupees,' said Jean.

The merchants continued peacefully to come and go. Round them the ragged porters, the exhausted rickshaw boys, the feeble, skeleton figures of starving children spoke of work and poverty.

★ ★ ★

Jean had an appointment in Mahatma Gandhi Avenue, at the jewellery business belonging to his opposite number in Bombay. This was the same man who had made us wear jasmine garlands at the aerodrome, and who had since put one of his cars at our disposal. This jeweller was famous in his profession, not only in India, where he represented several families among the nobility, but also throughout the world. He had contacts among all the great lapidaries. He had stayed in London, Paris, St. Moritz, on the Côte d'Azur, in New York and Hollywood.

I expected him to have adopted Western ways, but I found in fact that this wealthy Hindu, who spoke very good English, adhered strictly to the ancient customs of his trade and of his race.

He wore sandals on his bare feet, and a piece of very light white linen draped round his legs, in the form of unsewn baggy trousers. His large, burly form was covered by a simple shirt.

There were no outward signs of his status, and he was not the eldest in the family, but it was easy to tell, from the powerful, massive lines of his face, with its deep brow, from the tone of his voice, and from his measured gaze, that he was the head, not only of the business but of the whole family tribe of older and younger brothers, cousins and nephews who worked with him.

However, he could smile most attractively when he wanted to, showing his strong white teeth. He welcomed us with this smile, and led us through a huge room full of counters to an air-conditioned apartment, separated from the main premises by a wall of transparent glass. This room served both as his office and his reception room, and it also housed his most valuable pieces of jewellery. Sparkling in the showcases, or hidden in the safes, were splendid tiaras, lovely necklaces, rings gleaming with fire, shining bracelets for wrist and ankle. Through the centuries, the most skilled and patient craftsmen in the world had worked to produce this beauty.

He invited us to sit down on the divan, while a servant brought us strong tea, which tasted as rich as it smelled.

'I'm sorry it isn't whisky,' said our host, 'but you know how it is here.'

Prohibition was so strictly enforced in the State of Bombay that alcohol, including wine and beer, was forbidden even in aeroplanes flying overhead.

'All the same,' said the jeweller, 'the police are fairly indulgent towards foreigners. If you like to lend me your passports I can get you a bottle to take back to your hotel.'

He briskly called one of his nephews, and gave him our passports. Then he snapped his fingers and a servant came running to take away our cups. The jeweller's youngest brother came up and joined us. He was very dark and thin, with a pointed, intelligent face, slightly pock-marked.

There was a short silence. Then our host spoke to Jean.

'Now what are you interested in?' he asked. 'Pearls?'

'Not specially,' said Jean. 'The market isn't very good for us. At least, only for very rare items. Like those big studs the Chinese mandarins used to wear as a sign of their rank.'

The jeweller gave a slight nod of his massive head.

'We'll let one of our agents know,' he said. 'What with all

the smuggling after the Chinese Revolution it's quite possible—
what else?'

'Anything beautiful which isn't too dear,' laughed Jean.

'Of course,' replied our host, laughing too.

They were like a couple of soothsayers.

Then the jeweller sighed softly, and made a sign to his
brother to go and open the drawers and safes, complaining all
the while of the increasing difficulties which beset the jewel
trade. The principal source of jewellery up to that time had been
the inexhaustible reserves of private treasure collected by the
rajahs. Our host had been an agent for several of these princes,
but with the coming of independence and the establishment of
the Republic, the rajahs, formerly absolute sovereigns within
their own States, had lost all power there, including even that
of disposing of their own jewels. All this fabulous booty,
amassed by the dynasties over the generations, was regarded by
the Indian Government as public money. The only jewels that
could be sold by their former private owners were those which
the experts in Delhi considered to be of trivial value. Even
then . . .

A great jeweller in Calcutta, said our host, who represented
a maharajah in Bengal, was entrusted by him with arranging the
sale of a diamond. Everything was in order, for the stone,
though beautiful, was only of medium size. The government
experts allowed it to go through the customs, and raised no
objection when it was sent to England for auction. In London,
someone noticed that it bore a very fine inscription in Arabic,
showing that it had belonged to one of the Mogul kings, a
descendant of the original great conqueror of India. When the
discovery was given publicity, the diamond sold for fifteen
thousand pounds. It was only then that the Indian Government
began to feel regret that such an historic stone should pass into
foreign hands. Despite the blessing of experts and customs, they
imposed such a heavy fine on the Calcutta jeweller that he was
forced to try and buy the diamond back again, to return it to
India.

By the time our host had finished telling this story, which was
tinged with a curious sort of poetry, the long low table in front
of us had suddenly acquired a sparkling surface, like some
dazzling carpet. Poured out on to the wood of the table, or dis-

played in their cases, were jewels and pieces of jewellery, all united into one strange ethereal substance. You had to bend over to distinguish the various component parts, and then it made you giddy.

There were old enamels of exquisite craftsmanship, encrusted with sapphires and brilliants. There were rivers of diamonds, bracelets with clasps made in a design of mythological figures, worked in jewels. There were great necklaces of gold filigree, like lace, all set with rubies and emeralds.

Soon there was hardly any room left on the table. Yet still the red leather jewel-cases and the fragrant wooden boxes continued to surrender their secrets. The open cases and boxes were piled one on top of the other, while fires of green, blue, white, red and gold continued to flash from the magical combined substance they were yielding.

I could only look upon all this splendour and richness with a layman's eye. But Jean could savour its quality with the knowledge of an expert, even an artist.

Suddenly his breath was completely taken away. Our host opened the last huge jewel-case, and lifted up, to a level with his brow, a jewelled ornament which hung down to his waist. It was composed of the following: first there was a magnificent necklace of diamonds, alternating with emeralds of which each stone was worth a fortune. From this hung a pendant of three emerald medallions, joined together by a thick chain of diamonds. Each of these emerald medallions was a half-inch thick, and they grew progressively larger in area until the last one looked like a small paving stone.

'This was entrusted to me by the old Maharanee,' said the Bombay jeweller. 'She has permission to sell it.'

'But who on earth could buy that amongst our clients, nowadays!' cried Jean. 'Only the princes of Saudi-Arabia could dream of it, with their oil concessions, which are like treasures themselves.'

'As a matter of fact, their agents often come here,' said the jeweller.

He replaced the fabulous ornament back in its box. Meanwhile, on a counter, his brother was arranging fly-whisks even more voluminous than those we had seen at the bazaar, and with bigger and more beautiful pearls.

'I'll come back and have another look when I have more time,' said Jean.

'There is no hurry,' said the jeweller.

He helped his brother to close the case. His smile had gone.

* * *

However, the graciousness with which he had welcomed us remained undiminished throughout our stay.

He invited us into his luxurious house, which looked out over the bay. Here his beautiful wife talked to us with lively curiosity about Hollywood film-stars, and with complete serenity about death, which, to one of her religion, was a friend.

He took us to the races, where, beneath the burning sun, the soft lawns were alive with the brilliance of saris, flowers and turbans.

He gave us lunch in his bungalow on the beach at Juhu. The sea was warm and smooth, and on the beach snake-charmers were arranging mongoose and cobra fights, and young Mongolian acrobats were running along wires stretched between bamboo poles planted in the sand.

But everywhere the jeweller had two faces. As a host, he always wore on his lips his striking, charming smile. But whenever he took Jean aside his expression would become shut, almost stern. Jean himself changed in the same way. His freckles would be quite stationary, and his face rigid. This was when the two were talking business.

One evening, as we were leaving the jeweller's house, Jean said to me, with a casual air:

'I've heard that the leading jewel dealers from London and New York are both passing through here. We shall be seeing them. They're friends of mine.'

The English dealer occupied the most luxurious suite at the Taj Mahal Hotel—the royal suite, in fact. It had been taken for him by his opposite number in Delhi, who had also lent him two servants from his own retinue, as eagerly obsequious as slaves. He had also liberally supplied his guest with whisky and gin, in itself a remarkable thing in the State of Bombay.

In the huge hotel lounge I had an opportunity to observe these three members of the same profession, one from London, one from New York, and Jean himself, from Paris. They had known each other a long time, but this meeting had not been pre-arranged. If they were at all put out or surprised by it, they certainly gave no sign.

The ice tinkled in their glasses as they talked amiably about old times. From time to time, of course, one or other of them would ask some question about business, but it was always so lightly, so spontaneously done as to seem innocent. And the answer would be made in the same way.

At the end of an hour, having drunk well, we took our leave. Jean never spoke as we walked down the endless corridor. It was only in his room that he gave an exclamation of relief.

'Neither of them is going to Burma. They had me worried for a moment.'

'Why?' I asked.

'Because of the vanished rubies we're going to look for in Mogok,' said Jean. 'They might have met my informers here.'

I wondered if he were thinking of the luscious American woman, a bit over-blonde, but desirable all the same, whom he had spoken to in one of the bars, and who spent much of her time with the Indian princes. Or was it that little Siamese doctor, with the cunning face, whom he had greeted at the races? Or that tall Singhalese on the beach . . . ? But it was useless to guess. I had learned to respect the fierce discretion which Jean maintained where his work was concerned.

3

'SHIVARATRI!' said the chauffeur.

He was driving us through Bombay to the aerodrome of Santa Cruz, and we had asked him why the crowds were even denser and vaster than usual, and above all so much more orderly.

They consisted entirely of processions of which one could see neither the beginning nor the end. All classes of society were intermingled. The members carried sheaves or heaps of flowers, and had mystic signs freshly painted on their foreheads, in ochre, saffron, or vermilion.

'Shivaratri,' said the chauffeur again. 'Very important festival,' he added, and then fell silent, as though he didn't speak much English.

Not that it mattered to us. Our main concern was to reach Santa Cruz, in spite of these human rivers, in time to catch the plane for Calcutta. We only just did it: the engines were already running.

It was midnight when the aeroplane landed at the airport for the Bengal capital. Since this is a long way from the town itself, which is huge, the journey to the Great Eastern Hotel took an hour. In the deserted, dusty, ill-lit hall a very junior employee gave us our keys, grumbling the while. Then two bewhiskered ragamuffins got up from a shadowy corner, where they slept on the tiles. They were the porters, and they dragged our bags to our rooms.

In spite of tired muscles, and the fact that we had already discovered the surroundings of the hotel to be quite empty and dead, neither of us entertained any idea of sleep. The greatest and most secret of the cities of India, resting on the furthest reaches of the Ganges, stretched before us in the darkness—vaster, more mysterious, more wholly surrendered to us because it drew life now only from its night breathing.

We took a taxi driven by a bearded Sikh with an exotic turban.

It was a long silent drive, the wide endless vista of an avenue, buildings of magnificent, out-dated architecture, a park whose boundaries we could not see. No one walked the streets; there was no sound to give life to a scene of exceeding solemnity.

The pavements were covered with strange white grubs, pressed one against the other seemingly into infinity, and forming a sort of monstrous, untidily-ringed worm. Only when one of them reared up could one see that it had a human face. The heart of the ancient town that had once been the capital of India was abandoned, or so it seemed, to a race of slimy caterpillars.

As we went through the monotonous, sordid quarters, which, like everywhere else, were quite deserted and still, the drive seemed so long and so silent that we were on the point of returning to our hotel. Then, suddenly, by way of a little road which turned off on our right, we heard a noise of shouting—strange, piercing, and rhythmic. The Sikh taxi-driver took us towards it.

No change could have been more abrupt or more complete. From total silence we had passed into the midst of fierce tumultuous movement. In the centre of the lamp-lit square, a wildly excited crowd was shouting, singing, and clapping. It consisted entirely of women. They were surrounded by a thick circle of men, none of whom, apparently, thought of joining in. The women were young and most of them were very attractive. Around their necks and bare shoulders gold necklaces danced and shivered as they moved, their splendid manes of dark unbound hair floating out. Their skin and their features had a wild orgiastic beauty. At times they leapt into the air like Bacchantes, at others, without pausing in the dance, they bent right over backwards, arching over at the waist, as though offering their breasts and faces to the stars. Sometimes the revolving circle would break, the most frenzied flinging themselves in ecstasy into the centre. Despite their abandonment, never for one moment did they lose their expression of dignity, and of fierce untamed pride.

Wondering what the meaning could be of this frantic rite, held in the depth of the night in a remote quarter of the town, I spoke to the man next to me. He was a ragged coolie who spoke no English.

'Shivaratri,' he replied briefly. He never turned his eyes away from the wild ring, where the light caught now a brilliant garment, now a gold necklace, now the flashing whites of haunted eyes.

Shivaratri—this was the festival whose name we had heard before our flight to Calcutta. Air travel had enabled us to be present in the Gulf of Bengal at the peak of the rituals we had seen beginning that very same day on the banks of the Oman Sea.

An old soldier came up to us. He was a tall, sturdy fellow, wearing a khaki shirt and trousers. There was a rough honesty about his face.

'Welcome,' he said. Then he indicated the circle, where the shouting and singing and leaping were still undiminished. 'The women,' he went on in faltering English, 'have festival tonight. They must rejoice for men, without sleeping or eating—that is why they sing and dance.'

It was then that an old man joined our conversation. He was dressed entirely in white, and behind his spectacles his eyes were wise and steady. He spoke faultless English.

'Shivaratri isn't quite as simple as that,' he said. 'But it's quite true that, for women, one of the rituals includes the celebration of the conception of manhood.'

'I'll take you to the real festival,' said the man in khaki, 'if you'll come over here with me.'

A long way away, at the end of an avenue leading out of the square, we could see flickering lights and shadows.

I found myself in a quarter explosive with frenzied life; there was violence and mystery beneath the night-time splendour. At the time I was unaware that this district lay on the narrow reaches of the River Hoogly, one of the tributaries of the Ganges which formed the delta. Nor did I know that, in response to the call of the sacred waters, temples venerated throughout India had risen up here, even before the birth of Calcutta itself. But though I knew nothing of all this, I felt no surprise at finding this region swarming, in the middle of the night, with hundreds and thousands of men, women and children, while the centre of the town was like a city of the dead.

Jean felt much as I did. We were the only Europeans in sight, but, for some curious reason, it seemed the most natural thing in the world to be forging a way into the heart of these immense crowds of strangely-clad people, whose brown faces were more intense, whose eyes burned more fiercely than ever as they reached the summit of their exaltation.

Such was the power of this collective ecstasy that somehow everything seemed easy and simple and wonderful.

First there was that huge enclosure, open to the sky, where thousands of women, clustered together like many-coloured bunches of fruit, stared as in a state of hallucination at a man with great eyes of fire and a crown of jet black hair, who was shouting at them the cryptic words of one possessed.

Then there was that street—those streets—that labyrinth of streets—blocked with faces and bodies, streaming in torrents alongside the many flat baskets on the ground where food, flowers, perfumes and fetishes were for sale. At every step in this nocturnal market, amongst the cakes and food on skewers, the leather goods, and the materials, one would come upon little altars on which were enthroned gods with a hundred limbs and terrifying faces. Before them, suppliants knelt in the mud— young people and old women, quite immobile, whose faces, carved by the hands of starvation, of resignation, of religious ecstasy, were the most moving spectacle of all.

Then, suddenly, there was that temple. . . .

Its precincts were protected by a grille through which one could see an open space of grass, trees and flowers, which sloped gently towards the stone steps. The top of the façade disappeared into the darkness, but a soft ethereal light suffused the stairway of stone and the tall pillars. Spread across the grass, sitting on the steps between the pillars, were hundreds of men in turbans, and women in saris with veils over their hair, watching, and never moving. What were they waiting for? The dawn? The opening of the temple? Was it weariness or contemplation which gave them so benign and peaceful an expression? I could not tell. But the garden and the colonnade, with the colours and the silent shapes, made a picture more harmonious, more moving, than one of the finest works of Titian or Veronese.

And above all and everything, there was the river.

To tell the truth, the Hoogly, at the spot where I suddenly came upon it from a dingy back street, was nothing more than a very thin stream of water, almost a little channel, between sordid hovels. But what did that matter! This slow, muddy trickle was a child of the divine, immortal Ganges. People came out of all the alleyways to purify themselves there. It was impossible to tell what sort of people they were, because the river banks were unlit. Only the reflection of the stars floated faintly in the dark stream, as naked figures made their way into the muddy water. There were the silhouettes of veiled women filling vessels from the river, and carrying them reverently away. There was a procession of shadows, as silent as the waters. And there was a child who led towards the river a terrifying creature bundled in rags, so twisted and deformed that no one could have told its sex, nor even what it was. . . .

I came to my senses again in a square, in front of an open-air theatre, dark with spectators. This was like a religious festival in Europe in the Middle Ages: spiritual transports were accompanied by the desire for food, and the taste for wandering entertainers.

There was a platform bearing rather light scenery of silk and velvet. Two characters faced one another, dressed in magnificent old costumes, studded with jewels.

I heard the voice of the old soldier. (Had he been following us, or had he merely found us again?)

'The villain, the fat man,' he whispered, 'is a trader of the East India Company. The other one—the young and handsome one—is a rajah defending his country.'

At that moment the crowd suddenly surged backwards. Our guide disappeared again, and we were carried by the human tide to a great gaping porch which swallowed us.

So huge was this temple that even in the light of the flaming torches it was impossible to distinguish the outlines, or to see the ceiling. It was a forest of massive pillars and giant columns, a maze of halls and corridors, in whose vast spaces there was not an inch of room. Rags against rags, faces against faces, breath against breath: in inconceivable numbers the poor and the wretched were pressed one against the other. Fixed to the great walls were platforms of wood and stone, where in the half-light hung infernal swarms of crippled bodies and skeleton faces.

This was the temple of beggars.

But that night, the night of the holy feast of Shivaratri, they asked for nothing.

Some played upon strange instruments. Some sang songs with no rhythm. Others seemed to be asleep, though they were standing up with their eyes open.

Each group conducted its celebrations or its ecstasies independently of the others. It was as though a chasm divided them. There were separate tribes, families, sects, people of different races.

From the porches and the vaults of the roof hung entrails.

We went through the Courtyard of Miracles, with its thousand souls, through the impenetrable wretchedness of the pagan cathedral, until we suddenly came to two giant golden doors, firmly closed. Black against the gold, sacrificial viscera were knotted in foul garlands, blood oozing from them drop by drop.

Now ourselves a part of the great flood of human bodies leaving the Temple of Beggars, we were dragged on through another maze. Then we suddenly found ourselves up against a long stone wall. Through a gap we could smell some indefinable odour, smooth, ghastly, impossible to name.

The passage we were in led into an enclosure full of huge branches, with roots and great knots in them, and whole tree trunks, piled one on top of the other. A silent crowd glided past these fantastic funeral pyres. The smell became heavier, sweeter, more repellent.

Open before us now was the threshold which, over the centuries, had been crossed for the last time by so many human bodies. A hundred braziers were burning there, and on each of them there shrivelled a corpse, or what was left of one. The roaring flames were stoked by men whose half-naked bodies wove in and out of the shadows they made. The scent of the wood mingled with the smell of melting fat, burning flesh, and calcinated bones, and with the perfume of the huge flowers which decorated the corpses.

The flames rose and fell like waves. As their heat increased, the bodies made convulsive movements.

Out in the square we had seen the dance of the women. Now we witnessed the danse macabre of the corpses.

As I stood in the entrance two coolies brushed past me. They were carrying a stretcher which they placed up against the wall. On it lay a young girl, wrapped in a pink sari. Her lips and her cheeks were tinted with colour, and she actually seemed to be smiling.

Never had repose seemed sweeter, lighter, more lifelike.

The braziers smoked and crackled. On one pyre everything

had gone but a leg. On another a head still jerked. Soon, the flames would shrivel away the smiling young girl in the pink sari.

On the way back, we were both silent. At last Jean said in a low voice:

'I never expected to see that on our quest for rubies.'

He was silent again. Then he shook his head and said with humility:

'Whatever else happens, tonight will have made it all worth while for me.'

I had no reply to make. He had said all that was needed to express the deep feelings aroused in us both.

4

Two days later we were flying over the tall Burmese forests. For several hours we saw nothing beneath us but jungle and wild mountain scenery. Then a great snake of liquid, like molten metal, showed that we were passing over the Irrawaddy. At the entrance to the delta, Rangoon came into sight.

There are few things so exciting as the first encounter with an exotic city one has known only from books and hearsay. One is only too glad to make the adjustment of abstract ideas, so that they match the real scenes which are dazzling the eyes, and there is the pleasurable knowledge that pictures which were formerly incomprehensible are now rich in promise, and will soon yield their secrets.

As we went further into Rangoon, I found myself continually making comments to myself.

'The faces have a different quality here,' I thought. 'There isn't that intense, melting look one sees in India. The way their features are arranged, especially the shape of the eyes, the colouring, and the friendly, genial expression are all reminiscent of China. Another aspect of Asia: the Far East.'

'These pieces of light checked or striped material they wear round their loins and their legs, like skirts, are called longi. The women wear the knot at the side and the men in the middle.'

'People wash themselves fully dressed in the public fountains and then go about quite happily with water streaming from them, so that their clothes are moulded to the graceful outlines of their bodies. Water is a cult with them. They celebrate the Buddhist New Year by splashing and ducking one another—it's their great form of celebration, in which they take great delight.'

Sometimes, among the lively crowds, I noticed men moving with slow measured steps, though they were sometimes only adolescent. By their shiny tonsured heads, their orange, ochre, or saffron habits, and the beggar's bowls in their hands, I knew them to be bonzes, or Buddhist priests. I rejoiced in the sight of them, and gazed in wonder at the golden needles of the pagodas probing the sky, for this city is the world centre of Buddhism.

The first European whom I met in Rangoon was Roger Piérard, the correspondent of the France-Presse agency. I liked and trusted him from the first glance and the first handshake. He was one of that naturally tough breed of men, which includes explorers, big-game hunters, journalists and photographers, who regard adventure as their livelihood. Courage is a habit with such men, and modesty an unshakeable rule. They seek out danger, and even deliberately provoke it, without even being conscious of it, and their only wealth is in stories which they regard as quite ordinary and therefore never bother to write down.

Piérard was a tall, sturdy, good-humoured fellow, always active, and with a caustic wit. He had an incredible knowledge of his profession, loving and cursing it, rather in the manner of a Foreign Legionnaire, who has been in and out of the Legion several times. He had an amazing capacity for whisky and for the local liquor, a gut-searing beverage which could floor the most hardened drinker. He had been in the Far East for twenty years.

As a war correspondent, during the Sino-Chinese war, he had followed the Chinese army from Shanghai to Peking, from Chunking to Canton. Then he joined the Free French army as a secret agent. After that he had fought with the Chinese guerrillas and been captured by the Japanese, experiencing the horrors of their prisoner-of-war camps. When freed by the Allied victory, he was an emaciated, anaemic skeleton. After the Chinese Communist triumph he was placed in charge of the activities of France-Presse in Hong Kong. Eventually they sent him to open an office in Rangoon.

He ran it with efficiency, enthusiasm and daring, despite nightmare conditions. In a new State, still in the throes of its growing pains, he had to cope with inevitable touchiness, delays, and red tape, and with the heat and humidity of a climate which rendered almost intolerable the uncomfortable, poverty-stricken quarters where he worked. They were noisy, inconvenient, cramped, and picturesque, like the newspaper offices in India seventy-five years ago that one reads of in Kipling.

The A.F.P. in Rangoon was in one of the busiest streets, at the top of one of the oldest houses. The ground floor, a damp, sweaty inferno, housed the presses and the editorial staff of a local paper. There were stacks of newly printed pages, together with piles of back numbers, and swarms of half-naked perspiring workmen with yellow bodies and faces. Going up a litter-strewn winding staircase, with half the steps missing and the remainder none too safe, one came to a different kind of business on each storey: sewing-machines, exports and imports, rice and jute. Management and staff included Malays, Indians, and Chinese.

Piérard was on the top storey. The ceiling was made of old mats, blackened and rotting away. It was impossible to fix a ventilator to it. The heat was stifling, and the din deafening. A man with high cheekbones sat transcribing from the morse transmitter, which made a sharp crackling noise; the reporters held discussions in English, Burmese or Chinese (Piérard was the only one who spoke French), messengers came and went, the telephone bell rang incessantly, and was answered in shouts in all three languages. Piérard reigned over it all in his shirt-sleeves, with sweat streaming from his brow, his mood always divided between blind fury and roars of laughter.

When circumstances allowed he went off to seek adventure. Any excuse suited him. He would go out on campaigns with the Burmese army against the Karen rebels, or to disperse the Chinese bands on the Siamese frontier, who maintained that they were followers of Chiang Kai-shek, but were really involved in opium traffic. At such times, Piérard would live in the jungle by the side of the virgin rivers, sleeping under canvas or under the stars. He told me wonderful stories of his expeditions, and I envied him, while he envied me my journey to the valley of rubies.

Piérard's closest companion—they were, in fact, inseparable —was a young man with a slender, sensitive face, who, at twenty-two, could speak, read and write a dozen Far Eastern languages. He had also learnt Russian, just for amusement. His name was Jean Perrin and he acted as cultural attaché at the French Legation. As the Legation was short of staff, he also found himself in charge of commercial relations, carrying out some quite varied commissions from France. On the same day he might be giving lectures at Rangoon University and calling on the business houses, his brief-case holding at one and the same time Burmese documents, texts in Shan, silk stockings and brassières.

Some time before we met him he had succeeded in obtaining a seat on a military plane that was going to the Northern States of Burma. The tribes there lived much as they had done in the Stone Age, he told us. He had brought back a primitive cross-bow and some poisoned arrows. His friends, while they naturally admired the cross-bow, had mixed feelings about watching him use it in his rather cramped flat.

He too envied us our trip to Mogok.

There was one person, however, who regarded the journey with very different feelings: the French diplomatic minister. Not that he was insensitive to the fascination and romance of the idea. Monsieur Christian Bell was, in fact, one of the most cultured people one could hope to meet, and he had a lively and open mind. But it was his duty to look after our safety.

We had lunch in his house just outside the town, a cool, airy place decorated with magnificent curios he had brought back from India, and while we ate he revealed his misgivings. Mogok was in the rebel zone. Communications were often threatened, and sometimes completely severed. Political rebels and bands of dacoits made a habit of attacking cars and kidnapping the travellers, holding them for ransom, or sometimes killing them. A retired English colonel, on a shooting expedition only a few miles from Rangoon, had recently been captured and held for a ransom of one hundred thousand rupees.

Monsieur Christian Bell's advice only endorsed that which the Swiss minister had given Jean the night before.

'If you were my own nationals,' he had said, 'I would do all I could to stop you from going. We've had quite enough trouble already, what with the murder of a Swiss by dacoits.'

However, we hadn't come all the way from Paris to Rangoon in order to go back again. Monsieur Christian Bell could see that we were determined to take our chance, and, when he had made the protest which duty demanded, he passed on to other subjects with the greatest cordiality.

Before coming to Rangoon he had been posted in India for a long time, and he knew and loved it deeply, having a close knowledge of the language, the religion and the way of life. Since we were going to the valley of rubies the conversation naturally turned to precious stones.

Christian Bell had been among those privileged to see and

touch the treasures of the Indian princes. He had plunged his hands into those fabulous piles of jewellery, and had let them run through his fingers.

'There's one story,' he said, 'that shows you the quality and quantity of their jewels. I was at an official reception given by the Maharajah of Kashmir, and I remembered that he owned a diamond that was famous in France, because it had been the biggest in the Empress Eugénie's collection. When I saw the prince on his throne, covered with constellations of jewellery, I presumed to ask him if he was wearing the diamond. "Oh, yes," he said. "It's here." He put his hand to the back of his turban. The Empress's diamond only qualified for the lowest rank in his hierarchy of jewels.'

As he finished his story, Christian Bell gave that half-smile which is evoked by distant memories.

'I suddenly remembered a bishop I met on the boat to Columbia, which was one of the first places where I was stationed. He was mad on poker, and he was terribly unhappy. By the end of the crossing his opponents, of whom I was one, had won all his money from him and also his pastoral turquoise. We wouldn't take it, of course.

'I saw him sometimes in Bogota. He was leading a very dissipated life there, so much so that his superiors sent him into the emerald mining district to do penance. To get there was a seven-days' mule ride. I was very young then, and at the end of the year I took advantage of a brief period of leisure to go on the journey and find him.

'It was the Feast of the Immaculate Conception, and all the Indians who worked in the mines had to give a stone to the bishop. They were all emeralds. He made me keep one—a beauty too—in memory of his turquoise.'

Our host told us many other stories, some of them colourful, others moving. But it is the last one which has stayed with me more than all the rest. We were talking about Gandhi, about his life, and its close. Christian Bell's voice suddenly became more serious and more reserved than it had just been.

'I used to know an old man who had worked as a gardener for Gandhi—you remember that it was in his garden that he was assassinated. The old gardener told me how he was getting on with his work, hidden by a flowering shrub, when the murderer came up and raised his weapon. Gandhi said to him in a distinct but gentle voice: "My friend, so you have come at last." '

★   ★   ★

As it happened, I found myself on the evening of that same day in a place which offered to the spirit the same ineffable peace which pervades these last words of Mahatma Gandhi. This was the Schwedagon pagoda.

It was on the crest of a high hill about four miles from Rangoon. One could see it from a distance: a fantastic arrangement of strange cupolas, of curving arches and gigantic needles, all covered with fine gold leaf. It was a strange sight: the heart of an ancient and benign faith; a place of seclusion, open to everyone.

One reached it by covered stairs with hundreds of steps, made smooth and hollow by the feet of the countless pilgrims who had climbed them through the ages. It was bordered at each side by thousands of booths, where you could buy gifts, gongs, consecrated toys, parasols and flowers. At the end of a dark, gradually sloping corridor there was a pool of light, where one could see an object like a huge, soft flame. It was shaped like a pointed sail, and was the colour of gold and coral. This was the great ornament which crowned the central edifice of the pagoda, the holy of holies.

It is from the top of the steps that one can best appreciate the full spaciousness of the pagoda.

I found myself on a paved circular terrace, gleaming and huge like the expanse of a great river. From there, the central mass, shining with a thousand fires, bristling with a thousand needles, seemed to climb right into the twilight sky.

All round the terrace, guarded by statues of mythological beasts, without an inch between them, were shrines, chapels, temples and monuments. And all around, smiling serenely, were tens and hundreds of figures of Buddha, in every conceivable attitude, and at all stages in the stories and legends about him. There were sculptures in wood, bronze, stone, and marble, dripping with gold leaf, and with precious stones for eyes.

The ochre, saffron and orange robes of the bonzes looked as though they had been woven from the colours shed by the setting sun. They passed slowly across the huge entrance, with their shaven heads, their beggar's bowls in one hand or the other, sometimes making offerings of flowers, and sometimes gently vibrating the sacred gongs.

Dignified old ladies, each followed by a servant, would prostrate themselves side by side with beggarwomen. Then, after their devotions, they would each light a long black cheroot and go on their way smoking. Children ran in and out of the sanctuaries, and paralytic dogs warmed themselves in the last rays of sunshine on the sacred steps. The sound of bare feet brushing the paving stones mingled with the notes of the gongs.

There were no sudden demonstrations of faith amongst these devout folk: no transports of ecstasy, no signs of spiritual distress. They had a steadfastness, a benevolence towards the world, that came from within. If, as a passing stranger, one's eyes happened to meet those of a priest or of one of the faithful, one saw there a clear gaze expressive only of welcome and tranquillity.

On this high place, above a curtain of flowering trees, looking down on other golden needles thrusting up through the blue dusk from the town below, I was oblivious of everything I had read about the Schwedagon pagoda. I forgot all about the relics of Buddha in the sanctuary, and the fabulous gifts of the Burmese kings: the diamond-studded weather-vanes, the jewel-encrusted parasols protecting the ridges of the roofs: all about the other wonderful memories which earlier travellers had brought back. I contemplated instead the tiny silhouettes kneeling upon the slopes of the pagoda's roof, each one sticking there his own little gold leaf, on top of so many others which had accumulated there in the course of the centuries.

'They are acquiring merit,' said the young Burmese who had come with us, suddenly. He spoke quietly, but with a calm conviction.

I looked at him in amazement. Nothing in his life would have led one to expect this sure, steady religious faith.

He had recently returned from Europe, where he had spent more than four years. When he left Burma, he had been a Communist, and a Youth Organization had invited him to Rumania and to the Ukraine. The visit proved a deep disappointment. It wasn't so much a question of the Communist doctrine itself, as of the fact that in Burma these countries had been represented to him as the sole refuge of liberty. He found none there at all. On his return journey he found it instead in France. He settled in Paris, studied French until he could appreciate its subtlest nuances, took a course in it, and passed examinations.

His intelligence and judgement were excellent, and he could talk with the greatest ease about Malraux's novels, Sartre's plays, art exhibitions, the *caves* of Saint Germain, the debates in the Chamber of Deputies, and international politics. In short, he had so thoroughly assimilated Western ways (his knowledge of England was almost as extensive) that one sometimes forgot what his real nationality was. Then, all of a sudden, here he was showing himself to be eternally a disciple of Buddha.

This was not the only surprise he had in store for us.

As we were leaving I said how sorry we were that we should not be seeing him again, as we were setting out for Mogok on the following day.

'Mogok?' he asked, smiling. 'Do you mean the ruby town?'

'Yes, indeed,' I replied.

'Oh well,' he said, 'give it my love. I was born and brought up there.'

I was struck dumb for a moment. It seemed incredible that this young man who had been back only a few weeks from Montparnasse and the Latin Quarter should have had as his birthplace this remote valley, the object of those dreams which Jean and I had cherished for so long.

'Don't talk about me too much in the best circles, though,' he went on, 'because the leader of the Communist insurgents who are threatening the place is an old school friend of mine. As we saw eye to eye, we used to be great friends, but now we belong to opposite camps.'

He was thoughtful for a few moments, then his rather roughly moulded face broke into a child-like smile.

'There's a lake there. On moonlight nights the witches come out and float on the surface.'

I looked with some incredulity at this Marxist—for he was still of this conviction, though no longer a party member—this graduate of the Sorbonne, who stood there calmly saying such things.

'You're talking about a legend?' I exclaimed.

'Oh, no, not at all. I've often seen the witches myself.'

When Jean and I were alone I voiced a suspicion that I had begun to feel.

'Now would it have been that young man who started you off on the track of the lost rubies?' I asked. 'He comes from Mogok . . . he's lived in Paris . . .'

'Don't be such an idiot,' replied Jean. 'You know perfectly well that if I'd met anyone as extraordinary as that in Paris I wouldn't have been able to stop myself from introducing him to you!'

He spoke with patent sincerity. Once more my keen curiosity was frustrated.

I tried to drop off to sleep as quickly as possible, since we had to get up at dawn to catch the Dakota which linked Rangoon with Upper Burma, and which made the journey only once a week.

5

THE part of Rangoon aerodrome reserved for the planes of the big air-line companies was very like many other tropical airports in various parts of the world. The white four-engined machines landed and took off according to a strict time-table; the passengers filed out in orderly fashion, passing through the various offices and departments; their luggage and their persons were well taken care of. The whole routine was just like that of any other airport.

For the internal air lines it was quite a different matter. This fact was borne home to us when we came to catch the plane to Mogok.

There was no one to carry our bags—and we had added to our luggage some heavy cases of drink and tinned food. There was no one to pilot us through the mob swarming on the outskirts of the building. When we did eventually find the waiting-room I felt something approaching panic.

We found ourselves in a sort of huge courtyard, with a dozen openings leading out on to a cement runway. But there were so many people pouring into the place that it was difficult to distinguish the aeroplanes. It was an amazing crowd, both in dress and numbers. All the tribes of the region were represented, in their own costumes, complete with appropriate hairdressing and jewellery. There were Burmese, Shans, Karens, Tchins, Lishaws, and Palaungs. Mixed with them were Indians, Siamese, Chinese, Malays, and also several Europeans. There were dark blue tunics, longis and saris of every shade, and all conceivable kinds of hat and cap, making a diverse, lively picture where one glance could take in a charming Chinese girl with her skirt split up to the middle of her thigh, an ancient Hindu with eternity upon his face, a wild hairy man from the mountains, a silent yellow-robed bonze, and a peasant from the Shan States, with bare feet and dull silver ankle bracelets.

Despite the size of the crowd, there was nowhere to sit down. The room was divided by counters for the luggage, separated by narrow corridors. The result was that the travellers had to sit or squat on their heels among all the various bags, parcels, cases, wicker trunks and rucksacks full of their clothes, food, and household ware.

It was like a sort of fair, with the high-pitched voices of women and children rising above the general buzz.

As in all countries where land communications are slow, difficult and dangerous, the Burmese have very quickly taken to air travel. Airports have become as commonplace and familiar to them as bus or coach stations.

'This is a side of Rangoon airport that passengers on the big air lines never see,' remarked Jean. 'Our bus looks as though it doesn't want to start, either,' he added, laughing.

There were some slates hanging on the wall where the destination and times of arrival were chalked in Burmese and English. Ours had been due to leave some time previously.

'Fog,' an official explained, very courteously.

Outside, in the runway, there were ten Dakotas, placed at intervals. But there were no crews aboard.

The sky and horizon were, in fact, masked by mist, which made it oppressively hot.

'Let's go to the bar,' someone suggested.

There were very few people there. A few Indians were drinking tea, and a Burmese family was eating some spicy rice dish. Then a white man came in and demanded beer in a raucous voice. He was a bull-necked man of Herculean stature. One could see great knotted sinews under his white short-sleeved shirt. He wore a pilot's cap at a rakish angle on his bushy grey hair, and the face beneath looked as though it had been ravaged by wind, sun, and every kind of excess.

I invited him to sit with us, which he did, but only because he couldn't very well refuse. I tried to find out a little about his life. He replied with a rude shrug of his enormous shoulders. Then all of a sudden he became human: Jean had told him that I had been an airman during the First World War. He accepted another beer, and began to talk.

He was a Canadian, with a Danish father. He first took up flying in 1916, and it had been his profession ever since. He had been a fighter pilot, and then after the war had gone in for aerobatics at American air displays. Then he had smuggled illicit passengers into Florida and Texas, had acted as convoy when precious metals were being flown to the Far North, had been chartered by planters in Malaya, had founded an air line in the Pacific Islands, and had finished up by joining General Chenault's Tigers, the toughest band of flying adventurers in the Far East. During the 1940 war he had served in Chiang Kai-shek's air force. After that, he had become an instructor to the air force that was being formed in Burma.

'Well, now it's my turn,' he said, fixing us with the hard gaze of the natural recluse.

When the round had been drunk he got up and stuck his face against the dusty window.

'You'll be off soon,' he said to me, still looking out. 'They were quite right to wait, though. You'll find navigating here's like it was in the good old days. There's no question of radar, or even of radio. It's all skill and luck. . . .'

He pushed his cap to the back of his head and went out, a huge, solid figure, thrusting well back those great buccaneer's shoulders, on which he carried forty years of unsung epics.

When we left the bar, patches of sky were beginning to show through the mist. Our fellow-passengers were putting their luggage on board the aeroplane. Two missionaries in white cassocks were standing a little apart from the rest. The smaller of them had a round peasant's face, young and cheerful. The other was an old man with a grey beard, but he looked out upon the world with the light, bright eyes of a child. They were Frenchmen, and were obviously delighted to make our acquaintance. They were going to a place between Rangoon and Mandalay, for a religious festival in the Karen country. Their activities were confined to this particular tribe.

'And there are ever so many converts among them,' exclaimed the younger one, enthusiastically.

'It's because the Karens aren't Buddhists,' remarked the older man, mildly.

He had lived in Burma since the beginning of the century, and knew the people, their languages, religion and way of life through and through. France was remote to him now: little more than a very dear but distant memory. Suddenly his face changed, as though by an unexpected access of emotion. I followed the direction of his gaze: he was looking at my rope-soled canvas sandals.

'Good heavens!' he cried. 'Espadrilles!'

He repeated the word in a rather husky voice.

'Espadrilles!'

He shook his grey beard.

'I come from the Basque country, you know,' he murmured, in spite of himself. 'It must be nearly fifty years since I left there.'

His homesickness was the more poignant because it had taken him by surprise.

'Good heavens! Espadrilles!' he repeated.

The twin engines of the Dakota started up one after the other. It was time to get on board.

The old buccaneer of the air had been right. Everything about the flight brought back the old dare-devil days. It was a leisurely process, where height and speed were geared to the human body; there were unexpected halts; there was wonderful camaraderie. It's true that there was also an awful stench, aggravated by the accumulated heat from the metal sides of the plane. The sour scent of vegetables spilling out of the huge hampers thrown down among the seats was mingled with the sweet perfume of jasmine, the putrid odour from boxes of dried fish, and—worst of all—the air-sickness to which Eastern travellers seem to be peculiarly prone. And even then we were lucky, as the elder of the White Fathers told us, not to be travelling with mules, which often happened when the army required them.

But this inconvenience was just the price one had to pay for a journey which was as beautiful as it was primitive. There was the delight of hedge-hopping over the wild mountains and valleys. There were the splendid colours of the other passengers' clothes. There were their magnificent faces. And there were the bare landing-grounds in the jungle where, brought there by heaven knows what miraculous process, people waited for the aeroplane, and women came to touch the huge wings as part of some good luck ritual. Bonzes, helped by their disciples, climbed in a dignified manner up the steps into the Dakota, wrapped in their saffron, orange and ochre veils, which they took off as soon as they were inside, travelling stripped to the waist. At Mandalay, once the capital, where the ancient kings of Burma lived amid their fabulous treasures, and where, according to an old English sea chanty, you can see gold-fish dancing, there was a colossal gold and marble statue of Buddha, at the end of the runway, just in front of the gangway.

The sun was beginning to set as we approached Momeïk, in Upper Burma. This was as far as the plane went, and, as it was the terminus, I thought there might be a few amenities for travellers there. But it was even more primitive than the other landing-stages, and so deeply embedded in the surrounding bush that the Burmese pilot, though very skilled, had to make three attempts before he could land. After landing, as he had to return to Rangoon almost at once, he lay down under the wing of his plane, which was the only shade there was.

Around the strip of short grass where we landed there was in fact nothing except a few prickly bushes, and, behind, some hump-backed buffalo. The landing-stage itself was crowded with people waiting to meet the passengers, with travellers going on the return flight, and gaping bystanders.

Among all the gleaming materials, I noticed three men dressed in European clothes. One was a lean, very upright old man with a white fringe of beard. He was guiding the steps of an aged Burmese woman, who leaned on his arm. Then there was a sturdy-looking man in the prime of life wearing a patterned Hawaiian shirt and smoking a fat cigar. And finally there was Jean's colleague Julius, the veteran of Mogok whom I had met in Paris.

Here, Julius looked quite different. He wore a tunic over an open-necked plaid shirt, an old bush hat which gave him a rather battered-looking halo, and he carried a great knotted walking-stick. Even his glasses were different, for they were dark.

I was the first out of the plane, for Jean was attending to the luggage, and I went towards Julius. Although he was exercising great self-control, and his dark glasses masked the expression in his eyes, I saw the bones become prominent in his plump cheeks as he clenched his jaws and pursed up his lips like a person who has just had a nasty surprise. This didn't last long, however. Julius's features soon assumed their usual calm. He raised his cap—revealing the silver astrakhan—and came towards me, holding out his hand.

'Welcome to Burma,' he said in impeccable English, but with a very slight Eastern accent.

Jean came rushing up. He and Julius greeted one another effusively.

'I saw your family in Paris,' cried Jean. 'They're getting on very well. And your daughter has sent you a bottle of gin. She knows her old man. And so do I. We've got quite a cargo of booze—look.'

I had the impression that Jean was talking even more quickly than usual, as though he were trying to cover up some feeling of embarrassment or guilt.

Julius called a couple of workmen and shouted a few words at them in Burmese. They picked up our cases and went towards the bush at the edge of the landing-ground.

'Just a minute,' he said to us. 'I must just say good-bye.'

He went towards the old man, who was still carefully guiding the old Burmese woman. She was smoking a long white pipe, and the couple were now accompanied by the character who sported the Hawaiian shirt. Except for these two men, there were no Europeans among the people standing round the aeroplane, which was about to start its return flight to Mandalay and Rangoon.

Taking advantage of Julius's absence, I turned to Jean.

'Why did he seem so surprised to see me?' I asked.

Jean laughed. 'He had a very good reason. He was already very much against the trip, as you know, so . . .'

'So what?'

'I didn't dare tell him you were coming too.'

Jean gave me no time to protest against being put in the position of an uninvited guest.

'It'll all turn out all right,' he said. 'Julius is the soul of kindness, you'll find. Besides, there isn't another aeroplane for eight days.'

Julius had finished his good-byes.

'Don't say anything about my having had word of the stolen rubies,' Jean said, hastily. 'I'll tell him about it later, when I've got some more definite information.'

Julius came up and joined us, walking with short brisk steps.

'Poor Jim,' he sighed, indicating the old man with the white beard. 'He's been a friend of mine for twenty years. His Burmese wife is threatened with loss of vision. He's taking her to Mandalay for an operation. Nice and cool.'

'And who's the other man in the Hawaiian shirt?' I asked.

'He's an American missionary who . . .' Julius had no time to finish his sentence. The man in the flowered shirt, looking very chubby and sunburnt, came rushing up to us, his cigar clamped firmly between his thick lips.

'Hello boys!' he cried. He had the pleasant sing-song voice of an American from the Southern States. 'I've finished seeing the old man off. How about a game of poker?'

On this desolate landing-stage, at the very moment of our first contact with the high Burmese valleys, the suggestion, coming from a clergyman too, seemed absurd to say the least. But he wasn't joking. On the contrary, his face shone with enthusiasm, and with childish entreaty.

'Come on,' he said. 'It's a swell idea. It sure is difficult in this country to find people to make up a game. I've got everything we need.'

He waved his cigar towards a dusty and decrepit jeep at the side of the field.

'It's really my house,' he said. 'I spend most of my time driving about the country. I've got packs of cards, counters, a folding table—the whole set-up. Are you coming?'

'I'm afraid we can't, padre,' said Julius, his impatience making him almost brutal. 'We haven't got a second.'

'Oh, white men are all alike,' grumbled the missionary. 'Always in a hurry. You ought to take a lesson from the Burmese.'

Julius was already hauling us away. Even so I just heard the last sigh from the Hawaiian shirt.

'Except the Burmese don't play poker . . .'

A narrow gap had been made in the screen of bushes to serve as an exit from the landing-stage. As I went through it, I was startled by a movement in the bush. Hiding in a hollow amongst the prickly bushes was a Burmese dressed in olive green, and wearing a big hat like those worn by the Australian army. He was armed with a rifle. When I looked closer I could see more of them, well camouflaged with the undergrowth, and scattered over the whole expanse of the airport. They were all armed with rifles or machine-guns.

'They're soldiers,' said Julius.

'But why?' I asked.

'I'll explain later,' said Julius. 'We must get on.'

He was almost pushing us. His brow was more deeply furrowed than ever, and he was breathing more quickly than usual.

We emerged into a clearing where a great swamp stagnated, with pale grass growing along its edges. A few domestic humped buffalo, looking very emaciated, cropped the grass drearily.

At the edge of the cracked dusty path stood two vehicles. One was an ancient rusty lorry which started up with some difficulty, while the other was a modern American car, in perfect condition, and with our luggage already installed in it. The lines and the colour of this luxurious vehicle were difficult to believe amongst the bush, the buffaloes and the local women who were looking after them.

'That's an amazing bus,' cried Jean. 'Where has it come from?'

'I'll tell you later,' said Julius. 'Come along, come along.'

The chauffeur was a young Burmese with a pleasant, cheerful face, wearing an ankle-length check longi knotted on his stomach. Next to him sat a man of about sixty with very prominent cheek-bones and slit-like eyes. He was dressed in an ordinary brown European suit with a khaki sun-helmet.

When he saw us he jumped out of the car and began to bend his thin frame up and down in a series of quick little bows, in the old Chinese style. Meanwhile a fixed smile made his eyes look even narrower, and raised the sparse little grey moustache which outlined his upper lip.

'This is my broker,' said Julius. 'He understands English very well and speaks it a bit. He's been a friend for more than twenty years. I have no secrets from him.'

The khaki sun-helmet went up and down again several times, and while this was going on Julius whispered very quickly to Jean—in French this time:

'All the same, if you want to say anything important to me when he's there, do it in the language I'm talking now. You never know.'

Then Julius introduced each of us to the broker in a language neither of us could understand. What he said about me was much longer than his introduction of Jean, and I asked him what it was all about.

'You're a great scholar,' he explained in French. 'A famous expert on Buddhism.'

'But it isn't true,' I protested.

'Well, I've got to give some reason for your being here,' said Julius. 'Come on, get in . . . we've wasted quite enough time already.'

Julius settled between Jean and me in the back seat. The car made slow progress, because of the bogs. 'You'd better realize,' he said, 'that Mogok is a country on its own. No one ever sees tourists in Mogok. Still less writers. Your arrival will be an event. Everyone will comment on it, everyone will have their own suspicions as to why you're there. With Jean it's a simple matter—self-evident in fact. He's a precious stone dealer coming to the birthplace of rubies. But as for you——'

'But why the devil choose Buddhism when it's a subject I know nothing whatever about?'

'People are very devout here, and it will give us "face",' replied Julius, calmly.

Jean laughed. 'It didn't seem to make all that much impression on your broker,' he said.

'Oh! He's a Moslem,' said Julius.

'What's the idea then?'

'He'll tell other people.'

'Do you and he talk Burmese to one another?' I asked.

'It depends,' said Julius. 'We often talk Hindustani.'

'What for?'

'So that other people won't understand us.'

'How wonderfully straightforward it all is,' cried Jean, de-lighted.

Just then we passed the dusty old truck that had started out just before us. It was loaded with some rather thin mail-bags, bales of goods, and the passengers who had landed at Momeïk at the same time as us. They waved to us with a great display of friendliness, and we waved back.

'Where are they going?' asked Jean.

'Not far,' Julius replied. 'Just to the grocer's shop which acts as an office for the air line. Then those that don't live in Momeïk will go off—perhaps for quite a long journey—by buffalo cart, or on foot.'

Suddenly I gave an involuntary shout.

The road skirted a huge open lumber yard, and I had just noticed between piles of tree-trunks something that looked like a grey rock which moved. It came towards us, and I could make out a head with enormous ears and tusks.

'What's the matter?' Julius wanted to know, surprised at my reaction.

'Well, look,' said I.

'I am looking,' replied Julius. 'I can see it perfectly well. It's an elephant moving timber. You see them all the time here.'

We were now close enough to see the heavy chains which shackled the animal's enormous legs, and the tiny silhouette of the man—the *mahout*—perched barefoot on the great shoulders.

Behind this gigantic animal, which was dragging a whole tree, there trotted an exact but much smaller duplicate, engagingly clumsy and childlike in its movements.

'There's a baby elephant,' said Julius, 'and the older one is teaching him the job.'

'Let's stop,' I cried.

In East Africa I had more than once seen whole herds of wild elephants, but this was the first chance I had ever had to watch these fabulous creatures tamed and at work. Childhood dreams came back to me.

'Stop the car,' I cried again.

'We can't,' said Julius. 'We haven't time.'

'But why not? Mogok is only about sixteen miles away, after all, and the sun's still high.'

'I'll explain everything later,' said Julius.

But neither Jean nor I were listening to him.

We were leaning half out of the car, following with our eyes the progress of the shackled elephant so obediently carrying his master—a little brightly-dressed human doll—and followed by his tiny pupil.

* * *

The town of Momeïk consisted of a square block of dusty, gloomy-looking houses made of teak, almost all exactly the same, and raised up on piles to protect them from floods during the rainy season. The wide windows, which had no glass in them, were protected by slats overlapping with iron bars, in order to give as much ventilation as possible. They looked like hanging cages. The only buildings open to the main road were the shops of the Hindu merchants, and a few stalls with thatched canopies, under which people were having hot meals and playing mahjong.

We were passing through the most peaceful part of the town, with fine flowering trees in the gardens, when the chauffeur suddenly pulled up with a savage jolt.

'Nice and cool!' sighed Julius. 'It just needed this.'

Out of a side turning came a slow-moving procession which completely cut off our route. It consisted of men and women whose naturally attractive faces were at that moment lit up with joyful and benevolent smiles. They were all wearing very festive clothes, and brilliantly-coloured silk parasols swayed gently over their heads. To the rhythm of strokes on the gong they began to chant in high voices. A yoke of buffalo came into sight, with their shoulders and humps decorated with ribbons and flowers. They drew a rough sort of carriage, bristling all over with sheaves of corn, little golden temples, pictures and statues of Buddha.

'It's a religious ceremony. They're on their way to the great pagoda,' said Julius quietly. 'This'll cost us a good ten minutes.'

He took off his smoked glasses and wiped them nervously, revealing the deep-rooted, almost agonizing anxiety in his eyes.

'But what's the reason for all the hurry?' asked Jean.

'The insurgents—the rebels—the dacoits, or whatever you like to call them. It's much better to drive in the daytime.'

He put his glasses on again, hiding his eyes, but his voice was still anxious.

'You saw the soldiers round the plane? They're there because the authorities expect a raid every week when the plane lands. And do you know what the American missionary told me? Only yesterday—yesterday, mind you—when he was out in his jeep he was shot at.'

The broker in the front seat turned his no longer smiling face towards us.

'The dacoits,' he said. 'Wicked. Very bad.'

He seemed even more worried than Julius.

'The area between Momeïk and Mogok is one of the most dangerous regions in Burma,' continued Julius.

'Who organizes the gangs?' I asked. 'And why?'

'Oh, it's so complicated,' sighed Julius.

While the procession wound its way through the dust and the sunshine, with its carts, its parasols, its idols and its flowers, Julius talked to us about red-Stalinist Communists, white-Trotskyite Communists, green Communists who were neither one thing nor the other, and ordinary bandits who operated in the name of any side they liked.

'The country's absolutely infested,' he said.

'Oh, go on,' said Jean, 'things are never as bad as people make out.'

'It's not a question of people making anything out,' cried Julius indignantly. 'I've heard the bullets whistling myself. My own house has been attacked twice, this very winter.'

'What, your house in Mogok?'

'Right in the middle of Mogok, my dear sir!'

Jean put on his most innocent voice.

'Would it have been partisans, Communists, or just bandits who committed arson and murder and then stole the wonderful stones from the former dacoit who died so mysteriously?'

'Oh, so you remembered that story!'

'It was too fascinating to forget,' said Jean, in the same ingenuous tone.

'In Paris perhaps,' muttered Julius.

Jean tapped me lightly on the shoulder.

'I'm thinking mainly of my friend here, seeing that he's a writer.'

'In Mogok, he's a Buddhist,' said Julius.

I hastily changed the subject.

'If you're afraid of being attacked on the road, why don't you ask for a military or police car to escort you?' I asked.

'What!' cried Julius. 'The army! The police! Why, it's they whom the insurgents prefer to attack. I only hope neither you nor Jean have brought any khaki clothes with you. Because if you wear them, I'm warning you that I shan't go out with you.'

He quickly calmed himself, and said quietly:

'The best safe-conduct you can have is this car. It was lent me by one of the richest ruby merchants in Mogok.'

'I don't understand,' said Jean.

'The chauffeur's got a cousin amongst the insurgents,' whispered Julius.

Whether it was really because of this relationship, or just that luck was favourable to travellers that day, I don't know, but we accomplished the journey without incident. It was a route which would certainly have lent itself to ambushes, with its hair-pin bends through the mountain passes, the splendid treacherous jungle, the tiny fragile bridges of wood over the ravines. As we came to each hazard Julius and his broker exchanged fearful glances, but there was only one alarm. As we drove alongside an overgrown ditch, covered with wild flowers, a striped shape leapt out of it and ran across the road.

'It's only a tiger,' said Julius, with a sigh of relief. 'This place is full of them.'

He turned towards Jean.

'The first time I came here—it was in 1920, when I was with your uncle—the roads were naturally much less frequented. We saw an enormous tiger sunning itself, stretched right out in the middle of the road.'

Soon we saw a valley, dotted with hills, houses built at intervals on their slopes. Down below there gleamed a lake. We were in Mogok at last.

6

In the days when the kings of Burma were still like demi-gods, before Buddha had brought his wisdom to that part of the world, there was no human life in the high northern valleys. Wild animals and birds of prey reigned alone in the jungle and on the mountain-sides.

Then one day the biggest and oldest eagle in creation soared slowly through the blue wastes. This bird, who could gaze unblinkingly at the sun itself, looked down to find some food worthy of him. As he proceeded on his majestic and terrible quest he scorned beasts of many different kinds, whom he could have dispatched with a single blow of his beak. Then suddenly he stopped and hovered in the azure sky.

On the hillside there shone an enormous morsel of fresh meat. It was flesh of a quality the old eagle had never seen before, though his life had been spent ranging the entire world. It was the colour of the brightest, purest, smoothest blood. It seemed as though daylight itself had been made for no other purpose than to sparkle from its surface.

'Here's food as noble as my own blood,' thought the old eagle.

In one movement he folded his huge wings and swooped down upon his prey.

But though his claws, tempered and sharp as steel hooks, could pierce with ease the thickest hide, when they closed on this mysterious substance, which was the colour of a living heart, they could make no impression on it. Ten and twenty times the old eagle set upon it. But in vain. He began to wonder if his powers were declining in his old age. Yet when he tested his strength, the swiftest birds and the strongest beasts still fell beneath his blows.

At last he understood. This was not a morsel of meat but a sacred and peerless stone, made from the fire and blood of the earth itself. The eagle took it up reverently and carried it off to his own aerie, accessible to none, on the highest peak of the highest mountain.

And the valley where he made his find was Mogok. And that

stone was the first ruby in the world. And Mogok, ever since, has remained the only place in the world where rubies can be found.

This legend was told to me calmly and with absolute conviction at its birthplace. Its poetry is such that one might well envy the faith of those who believe in it. But science also offers a story of Mogok to inspire the dreamer.

The rocks in the Mogok valley are as old as the world itself. Like those of Ceylon and the southern region of India, they are the same in texture as the earth's original crust.

'They are composed of the same substance,' wrote the head of the geological survey made when the British occupied the valley, 'but they have undergone intensive modifications, through heat, pressure, invasion by veins of fire, corrosion from within, and other forces, Titanic in strength, and extending over so vast an expanse of time that it would be beyond the mind of man to imagine it.'

It must, indeed, have taken millions of millennia to form the strip of crystalline limestone where the precious stones of Mogok are found. It contains red, pink, purple and black spinels, the peridot, or olivine, which is the Mogok emerald, the red moonstone and the lapis lazuli. It even contains blue and white sapphires—no finer ones are to be found, even in Kashmir—and the star sapphire, with its six-pointed star in the centre. Above all, of course, it is the exclusive home of the ruby, the king of jewels.

The first ruby miners in Mogok found the remains of prehistoric animals there, and named the biggest of these underground graveyards *Hsin Te Kyaik*: the Vault of the Dead Giant Elephants.

As Julius had told me in Paris, Mogok preserved its secrets over a vast period of time. No definite light was shed on its history, hitherto concealed in myth and legend, until about the fifteenth century A.D. And this despite the fact that all the rubies of antiquity must have come from there.

At the time when the Renaissance was at its height in Western Europe, the King of Burma had a group of criminals deported to the north, well beyond Mandalay. They were abandoned in the middle of an infested jungle, stretching right to the mountains. To protect themselves against poisonous reptiles, insects and wild beasts they took to the trees and lived there. This may well have been the origin of the name Tchaïpin —the High Place—which was the spot where they first settled.

Tchaïpin now lies about ten miles from Mogok, and the ruby ground stretches between the two.

The deported bandits lived by hunting. One morning some of the younger men left the jungle tree-tops and went down into a small valley after some game. There, their eyes fell upon some brilliant crimson stones. They took some back to show to their companions, just for amusement. But the older ones were greatly moved when they saw them, for they immediately recognized the fabulous red jewels that the Indian, Tibetan and Chinese merchants used to bring from unknown regions. They realized that the young men had stumbled upon the hiding-place of the rubies.

They at once sent a deputation to the King's Court, which made a long journey through the jungle, carrying the most beautiful of the stones they had found. Their ordeal proved worth while, for the King of the Golden Land, as Burma was called at that time, granted them all a pardon, and gave them permission to return to the realm. But they chose to go back to the ruby fields, which they did, with the gifts, provisions and women presented to them by the King.

There was, however, one small cloud over the King's rejoicing. The region of Tchaïpin didn't really belong to him, but to the Prince of the Shan States, and the Shans were a strong and independent tribe. But since the Prince knew nothing about the discovery, and therefore attached no special value to a slice of uncultivated jungle, he raised no objection to exchanging this for some other land, at the request of his powerful neighbour. Thus the valley of Mogok was joined to the Golden Land, and a Royal Edict published in 1597 contains the first known reference to the ruby mines, which became the exclusive property of the Burmese Crown.

From that time onwards, throughout three centuries, the Burmese kings never failed to take a lively, greedy and tyrannical interest in the valley.

The miners were entitled to take from their findings only the smallest and dullest stones—waste matter, in fact, or ruby dust.

The volume was laid down by royal ordinance, and all in excess of this belonged to the supreme ruler—to the Golden Feet.

All the same, whether because of tendencies inherited from the original bandits who founded Mogok, or merely because of the natural magnetism exerted by the jewels themselves, theft and fraud were always rife in the magic valley.

From generation to generation the miners passed on the trick of breaking up into several pieces stones which were too big to come within their perquisites. And others, bolder still, eluded the spies and guards and smuggled their booty to the Rajahs' courts.

Terrible tortures awaited them if they were caught, extended often to their families.

The village of Laung-Sin—the Burnt Land—derived its name from the fact that during the last century, as punishment for a ruby robbery, all the inhabitants, including men, women, children, and even Buddhist priests, were imprisoned in a hut which was then set on fire by the king's officers. The inhabitants of all the neighbouring villages were made to come and watch, as an example.

It was all useless, for the miners continued to split up or to divert the finest rubies. There were some who preferred to bury them on the spot, and the hope of unearthing some of these still haunts Mogok.

This secret battle reached such a pitch that the last great despot of Burma, Mindon Man, less than a hundred years ago, ordered that all the bayon, or ruby soil, should be carried to Mandalay and washed in his palace courtyard. When he found that, after having been brought so far in buffalo carts, the soil had nothing in it, the King redoubled his atrocities. There are very old people still living who can remember the wholesale massacres that followed.

But outside the narrow region which extends from Mogok to Tchaïpin, few people heard anything about the amazing finds and thefts, and the large-scale executions. The kings of Mandalay had the secrets of the ruby mines so jealously guarded that right up until the arrival of the English in 1884 the Burmese themselves knew nothing about Mogok except a few fantastic stories.

As for the Europeans, those who had ever got as far as the

valley could be counted on the fingers of one hand. The first to see Mogok was the Italian missionary, Giuseppe d'Amato, in 1883, though he only passed through. Then there was a sailor who had deserted from the British Navy, and who settled at the court of King Mindon in Mandalay. Mindon gave him the task of blowing up some of the rocks which were hiding the rubies.

There were also two French prospectors who had the courage and good luck to reach the valley, returning with plans for a mining concession. Finally, however, the British, already in occupation of Rangoon and the Irrawaddy delta, pushed on to Mandalay and the high country. The whole of Burma was easily taken and became a province of India.

Mogok from that time belonged to the British Crown.

The many tales, true or legendary, which centred round the ruby mines fired men's imaginations and their greed. The effect in London was immediate, especially as this was the time when diamonds were streaming out from the Transvaal. Financiers, as well as ordinary people, went into a sort of greedy delirium, where they visualized rubies, even more valuable than diamonds, rolling out from Mogok in a crimson flood. Powerful bankers put up huge sums and secured the monopoly in exploiting the mines. When they floated the Ruby Mine Company there was a battle to subscribe the shares.

The most up-to-date and luxurious equipment was sent to Mogok, and adventurers rushed there from all over the world. It was like gold rush fever.

The powers extended to the Ruby Mine Company by the Viceroy were like those of the old East India Company. They could make their own laws, and appoint their own judges and military police. They had the right of imprisonment, and of deportation. It was like a state within a state.

But the modern machines and the administrators with their vast salaries were no better than the old feudal kings had been at making Mogok disgorge her treasures. Jail and exile were futile where torture and wholesale butchery had failed.

The miners of Mogok had learned the art of theft from their ancestors. It was in their blood; it was at their finger-tips. Their skill enabled them to evade all attempts to supervise them, and to render null and void the most carefully calculated plans.

Ignorance of the country's way of life, endless red tape, and rash expenditure, based solely on unfounded legends, did the rest. By 1920 the Ruby Mine Company went bankrupt, having lost twelve million.

The luxurious great clubs fell into disrepair. The splendid machines became so much rusty scrap metal. The water that had been pumped there at enormous expense began to flow all over the place, flooding the most profitable of the mines, and eventually forming Mogok Lake.

The British Government in India then left everyone free to mine as they pleased, between Mogok and Tchaïpin.

Then the war came, and the Japanese occupation.

After the Allied victory, and the granting of independence to Burma, the Government in Rangoon gave exclusive rights in the exploitation of the precious stones to her own nationals, licences being refused to foreigners.

This was the position in the valley of rubies when Jean and I arrived there.

7

M o g o κ extends round the banks of a lake, in the hollow of a
magnificent valley, 2,640 feet in altitude.

From every direction, jungle-covered hills and chains of
mountains overlook the town—or village, rather, for there can't
be more than ten thousand inhabitants. It is narrow in shape,
though it spreads over quite a large area. The long main road
bordering the lake leaves the jungle abruptly and ends in a fan
of short roads, all very steep and crowded.

The part of the town on the opposite bank of the lake is
much smaller and more poverty-stricken.

Pagodas stand wherever there is high ground, the newest of
them dazzlingly white and crowned with golden spires, the
others in ruins, their stones the colour of bronze.

The houses in Mogok are all alike, whether they belong to
the wealthiest or to the poorest families. They are enclosed by
walls made of overlapping slats of teak—a strong, hard wood
which grows abundantly in the surrounding forests. These
are either closed up or opened round iron bars, according to
the time of day and the season. In the full heat of the day the
houses become entirely transparent, but at night they are
completely closed up, for the nights are always cool at this
altitude.

They all have only one floor, which is reached by a very steep
outdoor stairway. No one lives on the ground floor, which is
used only for stalls, warehouses and workshops. There are still
a few thatched roofs left, of a beautiful soft mellow colour, but
most of the houses are roofed with corrugated iron. Though
this lets the heat through, it is very much more resistant to the
torrential downpours of the monsoon.

It was in front of one of these houses, in a central position on
the main road, that Julius stopped the car which had brought us
from Mogok.

He was the first to get out, and immediately had a hasty,
low-voiced conference with his broker. The latter's sun-helmet
went up and down several times and then quickly disappeared
from sight.

A small crowd, mainly composed of women and children, gazed at us with mild curiosity.

Then a little old man appeared at the top of the stairs. He had bare feet, a long fawn longi, and a dark coloured scarf knotted loosely round his hair. His yellow face was lined with tiny wrinkles, and in their narrow slits his eyes were still bright and lively, their gaze full of wisdom, subtlety and mischief. He came down to take our bags, smiling at us.

Despite the row of short brown broken teeth which it revealed, it was a smile of dignity and of considerable charm.

'This is my boy U Nyo,' said Julius, solemnly.

As we went up the steps he went on, 'When you put the prefix "U" before a name it shows that the person spoken of is someone of importance. People are very sensitive here. I extend this courtesy to my boy chiefly because of his age, but also to keep him. The Burmese in Mogok don't like being servants.'

The door of the landing opened straight on to Julius's office. This was the main room, looking out over the road. Its sole furniture was two tables, one of which bore all the necessary apparatus for valuing precious stones—a little balance, tiny weights, tongs and magnifying glasses—and the other a copy of the code dictionary that I had seen in Jean's flat in the rue Lafayette; an old-fashioned safe, a rickety armchair and three wicker upright chairs.

The rest of the house was even more primitive. A dark cell with a camp bed served as a bedroom for Julius. Then there was the kitchen—an empty space with a sort of camp-fire, consisting of three stones on the tiled floor. A corrugated iron door, which banged in all the draughts, led out of this into a corner reserved for washing, which was performed with the aid of a few old petrol tins. In an even smaller corner was a fantastic structure apparently made for giants, consisting of a large box obviously made out of planks, with a hole in it. As if to compensate, one had a view from there of beautiful gardens and a wonderful old pagoda.

When Julius had shown us all this he turned to Jean.

'I rented the extra room for you,' he said, showing us into it. It adjoined his office, and also looked out on to the road. It seemed rather large, because its only furniture was one very narrow camp-bed swamped by the mosquito net, and a rope stretching from one wall to the other, for hanging one's clothes on.

Julius scratched his silver astrakhan and spoke without looking at me. 'There are two of you now, though . . .'

During the whole of our stay this was the only reference Julius made to the sudden arrival of a man whom he had met only once in Paris, and whom he was now obliged to house in Mogok under the most difficult conditions possible. In fact, he overwhelmed me with hospitality.

I felt rather embarrassed, but Jean cried, 'It doesn't matter, I can sleep in your office, Julius. Then I'll be right on the spot for work.'

'That's fine then,' said Julius.

At that moment the landing door opened and the broker came in, fanning his perspiring face. Behind him came two men carrying a camp-bed, a mosquito net and some blankets.

The first of these was a grey-bearded old Indian in dark blue rags, wearing a Sikh's turban of the same colour. Despite his age, his carriage was very upright, and when he saw us he raised his hand to his turban in a salute, standing to attention in his tattered clothes with remarkable military precision. His splendid great eyes expressed a combination of boldness and servility.

'This is my sweeper,' said Julius; 'he's in charge of all the menial work.' He shrugged his shoulders. 'He's an old soldier from the British army,' he went on, 'and a hopeless drunk.'

The Sikh, guessing that we were talking about him, smiled at us with all his still dazzling teeth, bending upon us the full splendour of his magnificent gaze. I have never seen a face in which toughness was so combined with a sort of humbleness and guilt.

'And this,' said Julius, indicating the other porter, a Chinese with a fat, wrinkled, yellow face, 'is the dhobi who washes the linen. Now you know all the staff.'

It was the Burmese boy U Nyo who made the beds, for it was unthinkable that this should have been performed by the unclean hands of the sweeper.

And so the daily round began, amid the characters and with the setting of a dream.

When I got up in the morning I opened the teak slats just far enough to see without being seen. In the background the golden needles of the pagodas on the hills and mountains gleamed through the mist, but the lake was still covered with a thick milky vapour. Though I never saw the witches whose magic dances on the surface of the lake had been described to me in Rangoon by the young Burmese Sorbonne graduate, I could well imagine how he may have seen faces in this dense but fluid substance, which moved so strangely as though it were alive. From its depths, spread sheet-like over the surface, there rose bluish spirals and arabesques which hung for a long while in the air, taking on a half-human aspect.

Meanwhile, directly beneath the window, the little square was coming to life. From the ground floor I could hear the sounds of the bazaar opening. Opposite, the owner of the open-air restaurant was setting out the food, spirit-stoves, benches, tea-cups, and rice bowls. Just below the house facing ours, a Burmese was yawning at the entrance of the stall where he sold a well-known make of sewing-machine. He was a Roman Catholic, and they said that the missionary had arranged for him to represent this firm, as the price of his conversion.

The flat over his shop was occupied by a Gujerati Indian precious stone dealer. We could see him at his trade all day long. He would sit cross-legged on cushions at a low table and engage in endless discussions with his clients, always in the same position.

When I could hear that Julius was ready—he was always the first up—I would take my turn, going through the office, our host's bedroom, and the 'kitchen', in order to throw hot and cold water over myself from the old petrol tins. U Nyo was crouching in front of his fire-place of three blackened stones, his old face tranquil beneath the network of wrinkles, looking like the genie of the household.

Then he would serve us with mild Burmese tea, as precisely and carefully as an old woman. Everything that came from his hands had a wholesome flavour.

He had hardly had time to clear the last cup away before the parade of jewel merchants began. Julius always received a good many—it was the reason why he stayed in Mogok—but the presence of Jean, the chief from Paris, brought them in even larger numbers. From jacket pockets, wallets, bags slung round their necks, each of them brought out their rubies or sapphires. Then Julius's broker would set to work with the balance, the magnifying glass, the tongs. This business, which was in itself very monotonous, derived great variety from the changing expressions on the watching faces, and from the stories about people and jewels with which Julius, who knew them all backwards, regaled me in quiet asides.

While this dickering went on the grey-bearded Sikh sweeper, sometimes sober and splendid, sometimes rolling drunk and deplorable, swept out the room, and carried away the rubbish to throw it into an open-air gutter in front of the house. Sometimes he was accompanied by an incredibly beautiful little boy, whose eyes were exactly the same as his own—huge, luminous, and sad.

No one took the slightest notice of them.

The day passed like this until noon. We then went to see the most prosperous mine-owners and jewel dealers—the people, in short, who occupied the top rung of the ladder. Those who went out themselves were only the fairly inconsiderable merchants.

We came back for lunch, which usually consisted of a main rice dish prepared by U Nyo in a way which separated each grain, and wonderfully seasoned with spices.

The afternoon was again devoted to the dealers, but punctuated also with walks through the town. The streets, with their borders of booths and stalls, were quite peaceful. This was probably because so many of the men were working in the mines in the neighbourhood, but it was mainly due to the character of the people. No one shouted; no one hurried. The faces drew sustenance from a sort of inner smile, dignified and serene. Even at the big markets, which were held every five days, drawing people from the surrounding country-side and mountains, there was the same curious calm and tranquillity.

Yet Mogok offered an infinite variety of faces and different nationalities. There were pure Burmese and Shans, Palaungs and Lischaws, Maingthows, Chinese from every province of China, Indians from all the countless tribes of India, and half-breeds of every kind. For good measure there were also Siamese, Persians, Laotians, and Arabs. Whatever their origin, these people all had precious stones as a common bond. Of the ten thousand inhabitants of Mogok, six or seven thousand were occupied in mining the stones, one or two thousand in cutting and polishing them, and the rest in selling them. There were a few hundred people engaged in other kinds of business, but at some time or other these would invariably find that they could not help being involved in jewel traffic.

The poverty-stricken little stalls made up a humble sort of bazaar. Tools, household goods, materials, everything, were all jumbled up together. You could buy weekly air tickets to Rangoon in a dingy grocery-cum-bookseller-cum-stationer's-cum-haberdasher's.

At the lakeside, rising up from trees and flowers, stood one of the town's chief pagodas, and a big college for the yellow-robed bonzes. There were also two mosques in this same rather idyllic quarter.

The jungle began on the immediate outskirts of Mogok, providing a constantly changing landscape of mountains, hills, and valleys, wild and remote, peopled only by brilliantly coloured flowers and birds.

The administration of the valley was in the hands of about half a dozen officials whom one never saw, but who attended to the taxes, police matters, justice, and so on. It was as though such things arranged themselves, smoothly and benevolently. The people had evidently throughout the centuries grown used to living on their own, in wise little communities.

Their intercourse with one another was unmarked by any apparent distinctions of class or money, for the ease and courtesy of their manners smoothed away all such considerations.

I was moved most of all by their hospitality. I am not speaking of the most important merchants, nor even of the brokers, who were inclined to treat us with vulgar ostentation. But it was impossible to go into the house of the humblest stonecutter without being offered, tactfully, but insistently, highly-priced English cigarettes which had been smuggled to Mogok, and which the host never permitted himself to smoke.

At the business receptions the women kept a little aloof. But this was from modesty, not from servility. For there is no country in the world where there is truer equality and balance between the sexes than in Burma. Women hold important positions in business of all kinds. We saw their wonderfully tender, serious, intelligent faces, beneath their long shining black hair, watching round the tables at which we sat, or from the depths of empty rooms.

In the evening we would go home, and U Nyo would bring us whisky at sundown, which, in countries such as this, has an unequalled flavour. Then, one by one, or in groups, visitors would arrive: the close friends whom Julius had made during his thirty years of visiting or living in Mogok.

We found them a strange and fascinating collection. There was the huge Sikh, with a laugh like an ogre, who made his living selling rice in bulk. There was the Chinese doctor, with the eunuch's voice, well read, a lover of good food, mysterious. And there was the Persian money-lender.

They never touched alcohol, but, as they drank their tea in great noisy gulps, they talked about the news and the future prospects of the valley of rubies.

From time to time the jeep belonging to the floral-shirted missionary whom we had met at Momeïk would stop outside the house. He travelled from village to village with his cargo of Bibles and his complete poker outfit.

Since we preferred listening to stories to playing cards he added his to those of the Sikh, the Persian and the Chinese.

At this time of day there was always the sound of high youthful laughter in the main road under our window, as the slanting-eyed, vividly clad young girls came out of school. The colours of the sunset were mirrored in the lake. Jean and Julius would wind up their business for the day, then Julius, with that melancholy humour of his, would draw from his inexhaustible store of reminiscences. We would drink a last whisky, then, late in the cool, pure mountain night we would retire each to his camp-bed.

Sometimes my sleep would be haunted by a strange high-pitched melody. This would mean that there was a performance going on in the curious cinema underneath the house. Since there was no proper equipment for talking films they only showed Eastern films of the old silent days, so meaty and incomprehensible that the action had to be illustrated by a sort of orchestral accompaniment.

At midnight the crowd dispersed. Then the Burmese dogs, half-wild, famished, covered with sores, but untouchable according to the Burmese religion, began their chorus. It was an endless wailing, in which one seemed to hear all the suffering of the world.

O u r first visit, made not long after our arrival in Mogok, was reserved for Daw Hla.

The prefix 'Daw' is the feminine equivalent of 'U'. It signifies a person of age, or importance, or both.

There were three reasons for showing some deference to Daw Hla. Firstly it was she who had sent her American car, the best in the country, to Momeïk to fetch us. Secondly, she had been a friend of Julius's for thirty-five years. Thirdly, she had the most valuable stock of precious stones in Mogok.

However, apart from the fact that it was built half-way up a road which sloped steeply towards the jungle, her house, seen from outside, was exactly like all the others. There were the same overlapping slats of teak; there was the same very narrow stairway mounting to the living quarters on the first storey.

Just as elsewhere, the ground floor was only used in the day-time, and then strictly for business. At Daw Hla's it was taken up by a workshop open to the road, where the lapidaries worked. They were employed solely by Daw Hla herself. They sat mostly stripped to the waist, with their longis spread out round them like skirts, and their working equipment was very simple. It consisted of some little black sticks, a few small jars containing a thick whitish liquid, and a primitive sort of treadle which turned a circular wheel. A ruby was set into the end of each stick, held by a very hard brown cement. The craftsman plunged the stick into the liquid, in which diamond dust was suspended, and then with great lightness and dexterity made the coarse wheel brush against the stone. Occasionally one would pause and test the surface of the ruby with the highly sensitive ball of his finger, before resuming the delicate work. In this way, the ruby was cut into several facets.

'There's often the fate of some great jewel—some family fortune—in their hands,' remarked Julius.

He led us up the stairs, his broker following. The broker shadowed Julius, never leaving his side when they were doing business with the other jewel dealers. Since I knew nothing about the duties of this satellite, this, like everything else about him, seemed strange to me.

When we arrived at the long platform where the steps finished, the broker took off his shoes.

'It's the custom, because of the mats,' said Julius, 'but I think we can keep our shoes on here, as it's a very progressive household.'

Even so, the room, into which we went straight from the landing, had the traditional bareness and simplicity. Though very large and roomy, it had no furniture but a table and a few chairs of the most commonplace kind, all placed against the partition at the end of the room. The broker asked us to sit on these, while he went to tell the mistress of the house, Daw Hla, that we had come.

This gave me the chance to look both at the setting and the other people, for we were far from being the only visitors.

Opposite us, on the left, was a sort of pedestal bearing beneath a glass dome an exact reproduction of a pagoda, complete with golden needle, and with miniature flowers and offerings resting in front of it. Between the legs of the pedestal, shining in the half-light, there was a huge, magnificent block of rough crystal. From the side one could see the roof of another pagoda, made of the mineral itself.

But what interested me most were the people, sitting cross-legged on the bright mat which covered the whole floor, and all along the three windows, which were formed by the opened slats of the outside partition. There were about a dozen men, some wearing the longi and Burmese jacket, others the dark tunic of the Shans, and others the Gurkha turban. They were divided into little groups of three or four, each sitting round a copper tray with stones scattered over it. Their bodies above the waist were completely immobile, save for the movement of their arms when they took up or put down the cups of boiling tea from which they gulped noisily from time to time. An old woman, very small in stature, rather bent, and covered with wrinkles, went on her bare silent feet from tray to tray.

I was just about to ask Julius what was going on when another woman came in, preceded by the broker. She also was small, and well into her sixties. Yet, despite the smooth, round peasant's face, her unassuming bearing, and her shy smile, everything about her tiny person spoke unmistakably of authority. Whether she owed this to the rubies that glowed in her ear and at her throat, spreading over her jacket like a crimson rose, to the serenity upon her brow, or to the wise and impenetrable sadness of her eyes, I could not tell. Before Julius could introduce us to her—before he had even risen from his seat—Jean and I both knew that this was the mistress of the business and the household—Daw Hla, of whom everyone in Mogok spoke with a respect inspired by her personality as much as by her wealth.

With a shy and charming gesture she asked us to be seated. She knew no English, and was obviously very unused to meeting Europeans. She exchanged a few words with Julius, who said:

'Daw Hla is very sorry indeed that she can't converse with you herself, but her son who speaks English will be back very soon from the mine.'

A young woman came in and set a tray in front of us, with honey cakes, a tin of English cigarettes, and cups of coffee. This last commodity was both rare and expensive in Mogok and offered only to distinguished guests.

'Let me introduce you to Daw Hla's daughter,' said Julius.

M Yin U was her name. She had a splendid figure, a full mild face, the beautiful colouring of the Far East, and nearly as many rubies as her mother, though hers were mounted on horse-shoes, gold pins, and ear-rings. She blushed as she greeted us, and then withdrew again.

Daw Hla rose at the same time, and with a word of excuse to Julius went towards the men sitting along the windows and round the trays.

'She has to look at the jewels that are brought straight from the mines,' whispered Julius. 'The other lady is her older sister. She only values the stones, but there is no one with an eye to equal hers.'

We then learnt the story of their extraordinary lives.

Daw Hla was born in Mogok, of a Chinese mother and a Burmese father, in the poorest circumstances. She married a humble lapidary. Four children were born to them, one after the other. Her husband's income wasn't enough to support them, and Daw Hla had the idea of selling rice bought in Mogok to the miners on the sites where they worked, at a higher price.

In order to launch this venture, she had to borrow at the rate of five per cent, payable every month.

Carrying the rice on her back, she travelled forty or fifty miles a day. But she made a profit, and also came to know all the coolies in the mines. This was where her sister came in. Since her earliest youth she had had an extraordinary gift where precious stones were concerned. The two sisters used their profits from the sale of the rice so cleverly that when Daw Hla's husband died prematurely, Daw Hla herself could already support her family.

'She's handled the business and expanded it with something amounting to genius,' finished Julius. 'She's now worth millions.'

Some distance away, by the big glassless windows formed by the open shutters, the two women were squatting on the mat on their bare heels, examining in the last rays of sunshine the big rough stones that the Shan, Burmese and Gurkha miners had brought from the mines.

The landing door slammed, admitting a young man in a longi with a small check pattern, and a fawn jacket. He was amazingly thin and fragile in appearance but so finely proportioned that he seemed to have been carved out of old ivory. When he spoke to us in English, his voice also had this curiously delicate quality.

'Welcome to Mogok,' he said. 'I am Daw Hla's son, Maung Khin Maung.'

Then he told Jean how delighted he was that someone with a name so well known in the business should have braved the rigours of so long a journey in order to come to Mogok.

Then it was my turn.

'I hear that you are a great expert on Buddhism,' he said. 'I hope I shall be able to receive some instruction in it from you.'

I looked furiously at Julius, whose broker must already have spread the story. Julius never moved a muscle. Anxious to change the subject at all costs, I asked Maung Khin Maung the first question that came into my head.

'Have you ever been to Europe?' I inquired.

'No,' he said, mildly. 'And I don't know whether I shall ever have a chance to go there. My oldest brother lived in Paris for a long time, and represented the firm there, until he died suddenly. I'm the last son, and my mother doesn't want me to leave her. But perhaps when my own son is a bit bigger . . .'

Daw Hla joined us again, and her daughter brought us some more coffee and then came and sat down also. There were never the smallest noticeable gestures of affection between Daw Hla and her children, nor even of authority and filial duty. Nor was there any outward display in the relationship between the older brother and his younger sister. Yet, by some strong but indefinable means, one felt the bond between them, as full of trust, as peaceful and unchangeable as their faces.

Soon we took our leave. This first visit was purely a social occasion.

* * *

But on the following morning it was as a dealer in precious stones that Julius presented himself to Daw Hla. And so it was on every other day of our stay in Mogok.

These meetings were governed by an unalterable ritual. We would all four arrive together: Jean, Julius, the old Chinese broker, and I. As we passed the ground floor the lapidaries would look up for a moment as they stooped over their work to smile at us. Whatever time it happened to be there were always jewel merchants in the large room on the first storey, sitting cross-legged round the copper trays, waiting for Daw Hla's elder sister to pronounce upon their wares.

We had only to cross this room to reach the room reserved for important transactions. Though it was very simple, the furniture in here was in European style. One expanse of wall was taken up by a large table with drawers in it. Against the window was a similar table, in which white paper and pencils had been placed. There were armchairs and other comfortable seats, and a few boxes and safes were stored at the back of the room.

Our hosts would begin by providing coffee and cigarettes, and soothing conversation, full of courtesy and goodwill. Then they all went to work, moving over to the table at the window in order to be in a good light.

Jean and Julius sat side by side, facing the street, with Daw Hla herself in the recess, scarcely speaking, showing nothing on her wise, round, gentle face, but taking everything in and making all the decisions. Her son Maung Khin Maung, his quiet movements accompanied by the subdued rustling of his longi, the impassive half-smile flitting constantly across the delicate moulding of his face, would pass from one to the other, translating, showing the stones, giving the prices. In the background stood the old Chinese broker, taking no direct part in the business, but watching over it like a guardian spirit and trying to assist it by means of trivial attentions which he offered feverishly, with many little bows and monkey smiles.

Because of its novelty, it is naturally the first of these meetings that I remember best. Jean's face, usually so mobile, was serious and tense, almost severe, and his freckles were frozen. No doubt the responsibilities of his work had much to do with this, but also he felt stirred by the experience. Knowing as he did all the individual collections of the leading jewellers and lapidaries in Europe and America, which were the final destination of the stones from Mogok, he was moved to find himself actually tapping the distant source of them all, so ancient and so mysterious.

To the old Burmese woman and her son the meeting was no less significant, for the reverse reason. She, especially, having handled precious stones for nearly half a century, within the enclosed circle of the valley, found herself at last face to face with a leading dealer from the West.

They, of course, gave no outward sign of what they must have been feeling. Their sense of dignity, more even than their professional discipline, forbade any display of emotion. But, just as in some of the best documentary films one sees native actors who can express everything they feel without moving a muscle of their faces, so, with Daw Hla and her son, when their inner feelings reached a cer .n pitch they broke through, indefinably, upon their faces.

Julius alone was entirely at home. Forty years of his wandering life had been spent in passing from one end to the other of the long jewel road. During this time, his curly hair had grown grey and his face had taken on something of the patience and placidity of the East.

'We'd like to see the twelve carat first,' he said to Maung Khin Maung. Then he turned to Jean. 'You know—the stone

I mentioned to you several times in my cables, that I would like your decision about.'

Jean was the senior partner in the partnership he had formed with Julius, and as such he had to make the final decisions on difficult or important purchases.

Maung Khin Maung had brought a little packet of white paper out of the pocket of his jacket. He put it on the table and opened it, scarcely seeming to touch it with his thin, sensitive fingers. It was like a conjuring trick: there suddenly appeared, in the middle of the white paper, the first ruby I had seen in Mogok.

Jean was silent at first. His eyes, larger and brighter than usual, seemed to travel all over the little red stone, as though he were counting the facets, and absorbing its brilliance to the full. Then, without moving his eyes, he spoke in a husky voice to Julius:

'Could I have the tongs, please?'

'They're there,' said Julius, 'just under your hand.'

Jean's fingers were nothing like as delicate as those of Maung Khin Maung, but when he picked the ruby up between the slender tongs it was with the same swiftness and precision that Maung Khin Maung would have shown. He raised it to eye level and looked at the light through it, examining it for a long time. Sometimes he held the tongs quite still, sometimes he turned them this way or that. At last he put the ruby down.

'Ah, yes, I see . . .' he said to Julius.

Suddenly he picked the stone up in the tongs and re-examined it.

'Come here and watch,' he said to me, 'and I'll explain about it.'

But he was really talking to himself.

'You can see how difficult it is,' he said, with feeling. 'This ruby comes within a hair's breadth of being a really fine stone —an important stone. All that area—the main part of it—is very nearly perfect, but in the background—what you might call the heart of the stone—it's all misted over. The way they were obliged to cut it prevented their being able to hide the flaw . . .'

He rolled the ruby slowly between his fingers; the sunshine drew fiery gleams from it.

'But just look at the rest of it,' he went on. 'It's magnificent. . . . It's absolutely pure. It's pigeon's blood.'

'*Sang de pigeon*,' repeated Julius.

Maung Khin Maung didn't understand French, but at the last word he smiled and said in English:

'Pigeon's blood.'

And the old Chinese broker cried:

'Pigeon's blood.'

And Daw Hla herself, who knew no foreign languages, whispered in English:

'Pigeon's blood.'

It was like some mystic incantation; some magic password.

Jean brought the tongs down to a level with the paper and regretfully put the ruby down.

'I'll have another look at it tomorrow,' he said. 'Let's go on to something else for now.'

Within the space of a second Maung Khin Maung had folded up the little packet again, firing a rapid question at his mother. She assented with a scarcely perceptible inclination of the head. Maung Khin Maung, going out by the end door which led into the inside rooms, came back with his hands full of packets much larger than the first one had been. He arranged them on the table, undoing them one after the other until the coarse wooden surface looked as though it were on fire. Each packet contained rubies by the handful. It's true that the largest was no bigger than a cherry stone and the smallest only the size of a raisin pip, but in number and volume they were hard to credit, heaped as they were, one on top of the other.

Maung Khin Maung brought out more packets. Soon the whole of the table was nothing but a great sparkling sea.

'Look at that one,' breathed Jean. 'And that one!'

'But they're only the same as the stock I keep sending you in Paris,' said Julius.

'I know,' cried Jean. 'But in Paris I get them one by one, in driblets. All this is different. . . .' He seized me by the arm, seeming scarcely aware that he had done so. 'It would take years to find, cut, and assemble this incredible pile,' he went on. 'These rubies are only small, but there are hundreds of thousands of pounds' worth here. When they're set in gold or diamonds they'll make the wonderful bracelets and necklaces that you see in the big jewellers'.' Then, quickly, he suppressed his excitement and spoke to Julius. 'Come on, we'd better choose.'

The two of them then began to examine each of the rubies minutely, one after the other. They put the stones they weren't interested in to one side and arranged a piece of paper in front of them, on which they placed those they liked.

'Pigeon's blood,' they breathed, each time they found one.

A light, charming, fluting laugh sounded in my ear. Without my noticing him, Maung Khin Maung had come and sat down beside me.

'You aren't bored by watching all this?' he asked.

'No,' I replied. 'There's something fascinating about it. But I wish I knew more. . . .'

Maung Khin Maung took between the tapering fingers of his left hand one of the stones which Jean had put aside, and in his right hand he held up another, from those which they had reserved. He lifted them up so that they were both on the same level, the light falling on them in the same way.

'You can see for yourself,' he said. 'The one on the left is a dark ruby, too heavy and dull to be worth much—as commonplace as a cow's blood. The sun doesn't shine through it. There are some, on the other hand, which are too pale, faded looking. This, however——'

Maung Khin Maung held up the stone in his right hand, and his narrow eyes were lit suddenly with admiration.

'This one has the colouring of a freshly opened rose. The light shines right through it and yet is reflected by it at the same time, emerging ruby-coloured, purified, as by a fire which leaves no ashes. It's alive. It breathes in the sunshine or the lamplight. It *lives*.'

With a soft intake of breath, Maung Khin Maung laughed gently once again.

'This is what we call Pigeon's Blood,' he said. 'The Burmese word is *Ko Dwei*, and the Indians, who invented the expression, call it *Kabooterka Xyn*.'

Jean and Julius were still at their task. The old lady, still immobile, still keeping her eyes upon them, said a few words to her son, scarcely moving her lips.

Maung Khin Maung interpreted for her. 'My mother is very impressed by your friend's expert knowledge,' he said.

'But what about yourself . . . ?' I replied.

'Well, it's understandable where I'm concerned,' said Maung

Khin Maung. 'Ever since I was six, during any spare time that was left over from my studies, my mother and my aunt have made it a rule to teach me all they could about precious stones. And ever since I finished my studies, jewels have been my profession.'

He looked at me with respect, and went on:

'My studies have been devoted, above all, to the teaching of the Master, and since you are an expert on Buddhism . . .'

The very word induced a state of panic.

'The truth is,' I blurted out suddenly, 'that I've come here to write a book about the valley of rubies.'

The narrow, shrewd, intelligent eyes slid towards Julius.

'M. Julius is a good friend,' said Maung Khin Maung, with a gentle smile.

Did one understand from that that Julius had wanted to give me 'face', or to honour the people of Mogok? And was Maung Khin Maung speaking of the fact of his having brought me there, or of the false story? It was impossible to tell. Besides, Jean had risen to his feet.

'That'll do for today,' he said.

The rubies he had chosen were gathered up into three packets. These were then sealed with sealing wax, to which Jean applied the seal on the ring he wore.

'Now no one else has the right to see the stones before we've given our reply,' explained Jean.

'We aren't married yet,' added Julius, 'only engaged.'

The meetings which followed resembled the first one in every way, except that sometimes the fat packets contained sapphires as well as rubies. With these two dazzling alternatives, the table-top sometimes became a field of ethereally glittering corn-flowers, and sometimes a carpet sown with little constellations of crimson stars.

Jean continued in his task of choosing the stones, always with the same untiring precision. But from time to time he would question Julius in a low voice.

'Isn't there anything else? Aren't there any rare pieces?'

And always Julius, as imperturbable and patient as our hosts, would make the same reply:

'You never know. Just let's wait a bit.'

As time went on, a more intimate and familiar atmosphere

had begun to prevail round the table. This was due mainly to Jean's own manner. He had instinctively avoided any attempt to play the weighty impenetrable merchant, turned to stone by his own sense of importance. Instead, in this friendly, hospitable house, he joked with Maung Khin Maung as with a friend and equal, and respectfully paid court to Daw Hla. When any stone excited his enthusiasm he showed his pleasure without reserve.

Trust engendered trust. They talked about their family, and produced the family for us to see. Maung Khin Maung's three-year-old daughter, a strange, slanting-eyed little doll with a mop of jet black hair, was presented to us. Then his wife brought in their three-month-old son, the pride of the household.

Maung Khin Maung's wife, they told us, was the daughter of a great mine-owner in Tchaïpin, at the other end of the valley, and Daw Hla's eldest daughter was married to one of the chief jewel merchants in Mogok. He came and visited us at his mother-in-law's house.

The youngest daughter, who was still unmarried, and whom we had already met, also worked in the family business. She was in charge of the semi-precious stones, such as zircons and peridots, which were found in abundance in the mines. These—blue, white, green, yellow, orange, and pink, wonderfully limpid and exquisitely coloured—were arranged by the young girl with subtle artistry, forming flower-heads, bees, and magic wheels, as they lay in their cases.

One morning, at a word from Daw Hla, who sat as usual at the end of the table, immobile and benevolently watchful, Maung Khin Maung said to Jean, with apparent casualness:

'Would you like to see some star stones?'

Jean almost started up out of his chair.

'Wouldn't I just,' he cried. 'Why ever haven't you shown them to me before?'

Maung Khin Maung smiled that shrewd, scarcely perceptible, always charming smile of his and gave an enigmatic reply.

'Because they weren't on view just then,' he said, smoothly.

He went towards the inner rooms where the treasures were kept, while Daw Hla, gentle and serene as ever, continued to gaze at the table.

'They've told me about these stones,' murmured Julius to

Jean, 'but it's because you're here that they've decided to bring them out.'

I inquired what the star stones were.

'When they're really beautiful examples you can get top prices for them in America. The women there are mad on them,' said Julius.

'Yes, but what are they like?'

Maung Khin Maung had returned.

'You'll see,' said Jean.

And I saw.

The traditional little white paper packets were half full of rubies and half of sapphires. In the heart of every stone there was a sort of glittering fire, more golden than gold itself, more brilliant than a diamond—a six-pointed star, each point of which shone with a mysterious light.

'Do you see?' said Jean.

As he spoke he flashed on to the stones a powerful electric torch with which Maung Khin Maung had equipped him. It was the best light for showing up the stars.

'Yes, I do see,' I replied quietly. I was fascinated by the way the stars were lodged in the heart of the already brilliant jewels.

One of the rubies was particularly magnificent. It was a pigeon's blood stone (by now I understood the significance of the expression) and seemed to hold within it its own sun, whose rays penetrated right through the inside of the stone.

'This has just come from the workroom,' said Maung Khin Maung, with a sort of reverent gratitude. 'You know what that means to us.'

Julius turned to me to explain. 'You can see these stars in hundreds of stones, when they're still in their rough, uncut state, but after cutting there may be only one stone in the whole lot which still shows its star.'

'What are they asking for these?' said Jean briskly.

Julius put the question to Maung Khin Maung, who passed it on to his mother. Daw Hla thought for a moment and then gave the price in Burmese. The broker seemed to catch it in mid-flight and to throw it hastily to Julius in Hindustani. Julius bent over and whispered it into Jean's ear.

'But that's very high,' said Jean in French. 'They've almost exceeded the prices the American dealers ask for them.'

Julius shrugged his shoulders and raised his eyebrows simultaneously. He compressed his lips with a resigned expression.

'They're not too keen on selling their best pieces—nor even on showing them, as you've seen.'

'But why not?'

'Well, it's hard to say exactly. But really important finds are certainly growing rarer and rarer in the mines. And then the Burmese currency is unstable, also there are the bandits, and a star ruby is easier to carry about than a bundle of notes.'

'Well, why have they shown them, then?' asked Jean.

'To give themselves "face" before an expert,' Julius replied. 'And also as a gesture of friendship towards you.'

But it was not until the end of our stay in Mogok that we understood the full extent of their acceptance of Jean as a friend. We spoke of our departure to Daw Hla with regret, for we had grown very fond of the old Burmese lady, although we had not been able to talk to her, and her only communication with us had been her slow, wise, gentle glances. She must have guessed how we felt towards her, and been touched by our regard. As she had so often done before, she turned to her son with some brief request.

Once again Maung Khin Maung disappeared into the interior. This time, however, he didn't come back alone. Daw Hla's elder sister was with him. We were very surprised to see her, for she had never been present at the family business meetings. We had had no chance to do more than glimpse her in the big room, a slender, silent, furtive shadow, stooping over the stones the miners brought. We were struck suddenly with the fact that, despite her lack of stature, her self-effacing shyness and her simple clothes, she had, like Daw Hla herself, an innate dignity of her own. We were further surprised to observe that she was carrying an enormous but very commonplace flat dish, with half the enamel chipped off.

She put it down on the table. Almost at once Jean let out a strangled cry:

'But Julius—why, there can't be anything like that in the world!'

Julius, with an illogical nervous reflex, took off his glasses so that he could see better.

'I've been coming here for thirty years and they never gave me even a hint that they had anything like that.'

I moved away from Jean and Julius and bent over the dish myself. Between its cracked and shabby edges I saw, not precious stones, but a dozen heavy and rough-hewn blocks of mineral. The colour and consistency were extraordinary: the surface gave off a milky light, like an opal, and through it one could see a sort of fluid, looking at times soft and blue, like the mildest daytime sky, and at others seeming to hold all the colours of the dawn.

I turned to Jean. 'Will you tell me . . .'

He gave me no chance to finish.

'That's the rough stone,' he cried. 'It's how precious stones look when they're still in their natural state. That's how they are when they're hidden in the beds of rock. But I've never seen anything in my life of such unusual size and quality—of such amazing promise!'

He picked up the great lumps of stone one by one and held them to the light.

'Look at this!' he shouted each time. 'Julius—come and look. It's incredible. Rubies surrounded by sapphires!'

Then they were both silent as Maung Khin Maung spoke in his frail, thin voice.

'My aunt chose them,' he said. 'There's no one with a surer eye in the whole valley between Mogok and Tchaïpin.'

I glanced at the old woman, and at her eyes, calm and dulled by long use. She murmured a few barely distinguishable words. Daw Hla made an assenting movement of her head, and Maung Khin Maung also inclined his ivory-carved countenance.

'My aunt is very wise,' he said. 'She says we must wait and see what they'll be like after cutting.'

With his usual kindness and courtesy he turned towards my ignorant and uninitiated self.

'Here we're in the presence of the great unknown,' he said. 'This is the real gamble. No experts, however knowledgeable, can truly predict what will emerge from the rough stones. No eye, however skilled, can see the inner mistiness—what we call the flaw. This only shows at the end, when the stone has been extracted from its gangue, or outer casing of mineral.'

'And then,' added Julius, 'the light no longer shines through it. The ruby's dead—it may be worth no more than a half or a third of what you've paid for it. And then . . .' He whistled in deprecation.

Maung Khin Maung pointed one of his thin fingers at the blue and crimson-veined stone which Jean still held.

'The work that will involve will be terribly difficult,' he said. 'It will take months. And during those months I shall be supervising the craftsmen in fear and trembling. They will be working on it by candlelight, which is the best, first sawing along the fissures of the mineral deposit, then establishing the facets, then polishing them—and after all that we may, perhaps, find a flaw.'

The old Chinese broker joined in at that point. His wrinkles and his grimaces expressed just one thing—gambling fever.

'On the other hand,' said he, 'if the cutting turns out as may be hoped, the stone that emerges will be worth more than the most famous rubies in the collection of U Min Paw.'

At the mention of this name Julius raised his eyebrows and wiped his glasses. The old broker himself looked as though he regretted having spoken it in a moment of excitement.

I turned to Maung Khin Maung. 'Who is U Min Paw?' I asked.

'He is no more,' he replied. 'And no one knows what has become of his stones.' He spoke with what seemed to me a somewhat exaggerated air of detachment.

'Oh yes,' murmured Jean, apparently deeply absorbed in examining one of the uncut rubies. 'I think that was the story Julius told us in Paris.'

Then Jean, in an apparently absent-minded and mechanical way, repeated the name of the former highway robber two or three times. 'U Min Paw . . . U Min Paw . . .' I knew perfectly well that he was really trying to impress it upon his memory.

Suddenly Jean put the stone back on the dish.

'What do you consider it's worth, in its natural state?' he asked. 'Ten million francs?'

Maung Khin Maung took a pencil and turned this into Burmese rupees. Then he said quietly: 'Twice that.'

'For once I won't bargain,' said Jean. 'And if you would really like me to, I'll be willing to go half shares in the gamble.'

Julius took off his glasses.

'Nice and cool,' he muttered. He never liked playing with Fate.

The exquisite laughter of Maung Khin Maung was all the answer Jean received. Before the former had had time to explain to his mother what Jean had said she had sent him one of her questioning glances. He translated the offer. A smile of great charm lighted the old lady's face, usually so reserved. Then she spoke to Maung Khin Maung, and he interpreted her words back to Jean.

'My mother is very deeply touched that you should show such confidence in us,' he said. 'But she feels that if she were to accept your offer she would cause her elder sister to lose face. For it has always been she who chooses the rough stones.'

The older of the two sisters picked up the dish and carried it into the depths of the house without a word, her bare feet flagging a little as she walked across the mat.

9

IT WAS difficult to get used to them at first. They would come without knocking or announcing themselves in any way. The outside landing door led straight into Julius's office, and, since it was customary to remove the shoes before entering, they would appear without a sound, like ghosts. I would come out of my bedroom or the washing recess and find that the office, empty only a few minutes before, was suddenly full of men of every age, in every kind of garb. There might be one sitting on a chair, another on Jean's bed, another squatting on the floor. And they would all be waiting, immobile and entirely unhurried, as though they had their whole lives before them and nothing else to do.

They were all jewel dealers. Of course, even in their dreams they owned nothing to compare either with the openly displayed stock or the secret resources of Daw Hla and her family. Some of them lived from hand to mouth. Even so, they represented a proportion of the one thousand five hundred recognized traders who—out of the population of ten thousand—lived solely by the sale of precious stones.

The most prosperous bought the already cut stones which the poorest dealers obtained in their natural state from some of the needy miners. These would then be offered to someone with a house of their own, or who had contacts among foreign buyers, or some other outlet.

Julius, who always followed the traditions of Mogok, held a sort of open market in his office. The arrival of Jean, the important dealer from Paris, had made it the busiest centre of the kind in the town.

The procession began very early, and lasted till midday, being resumed again after lunch. In most instances, business was done very quickly. Julius would glance at the stones and give his refusal without letting it get as far as Jean, who was sitting the other side of the table. The dealer would accept the decision with a peaceful smile, fold up the packet and go off on his rounds again.

But when a stone (usually a small sapphire, for these were

neither so rare nor so valuable as rubies) attracted the attention of both Julius and Jean, the whole ceremony would take place. First of all one or other of them would instinctively hold the stone against his cheek, for precious minerals have the property of growing warm when they come into contact with the skin. Then the magnifying glass, the tongs and the balance would all come into play. Then came the most decisive phase in it all: the discussion of the price.

The first such discussion amazed me. I had expected a vehement argument, accompanied by much indignant gesticulating, like the bargaining in the bazaar. But not a word was spoken. Julius just made a sign to the broker, who immediately rushed towards the dealer and threw over his right hand a scarf which he was holding ready. Then he slid his own hand under the scarf which immediately began to shake and undulate.

'What's going on?' I inquired of Julius.

'They're bargaining,' he replied.

'But how?'

'By touching their palms and fingers and joints together,' he replied. 'Each part of the hand represents a fixed price—it's all according to an old established convention known to all the jewel dealers in the East.'

'Can you count like that?' I wanted to know. 'Quickly?'

'As quickly as anyone else,' laughed Julius. 'I learnt to do it in Arabia in about 1910, and also in the big pearl market in the Gulf of Bahrein. The system was invented there, because the Arabs, Indians and Persians had no other way of communicating with one another.'

The deaf and dumb dialogue under the green scarf pursued its course. Then suddenly the old Chinaman let out a loud cry, made the scarf vanish like a conjurer and slapped his palm smartly on to that of the dealer. Whereupon the dealer gave him a sapphire, which he passed on to Julius. Thus the deal was concluded.

For one purchase, how many other people were sent away, after fetching out from the pocket of a waistcoat or jacket, from a fold in the turban, or from a bag hung round the neck, a poor quality stone which represented their all! I was amazed at Julius's unlimited patience. I wondered whether he couldn't have done some preliminary screening by means of their general appearance, their clothes, or their demeanour, for he knew everyone in Mogok.

'In this country you never know,' he sighed, when I raised the question. 'The most extraordinary scoops arise sometimes. I once bought a wonderful star ruby from an Arab doctor who had no patients at all. And another time the son of my dohbi—the laundryman—sold me a fine sapphire. And even the sweeper himself, that drunken untouchable old beggar—well, from time to time, he brings me some quite passable stones.'

'But where does he get them from?' I asked.

Julius made his favourite gesture of shrugging the shoulders and raising the eyebrows simultaneously.

'You can try asking him,' he replied. 'His grandson found it when he was playing with some of the waste products from a mine. . . . Or he won it gambling with someone even drunker than himself.' Julius sighed again. 'Everybody is a dealer in stones here.'

★   ★   ★

There was only one amongst all the important jewel merchants in Mogok who didn't wish us to visit him, as would have been normal with one of his commercial standing. He arrived in person at Julius's office to show Jean a beautiful ruby that had come from one of his own mines. He did, it is true, make a special appointment beforehand, and he was escorted by his nephew, who acted as his broker, and who watched over him zealously in order to anticipate his smallest wish.

The dealer himself was an affable, simple fellow. He wore a longi and a neutral-coloured jacket, made of cheap material. He effaced himself completely so that Jean and Julius should precede him as they entered the room. He made innocent little jokes, and he pressed upon each of us the inky black Burmese cheroots which he smoked all the while.

Yet he had one very strange characteristic. Whenever he smiled—which was often—the smile involved only his pale lips and the deep wrinkles with which his dry, bony face was engraved. His gaze itself was always troubled, anxious, almost anguished, a curious thing in a man of substance, especially one belonging to a race characterized above all by serenity. And besides the haunted, hunted eyes, his face wore another sign of inner turmoil. A nervous twitch jerked up the whole of the left cheek in a series of regular spasms, extending from the angle of the grizzled eyebrow to the point of the tapered chin.

And however else he was occupied, during the whole examination of the ruby, while it passed between Jean, Julius and the old Chinese broker, the old fellow never for a second allowed it to escape from his furtive, side-long gaze, in the depths of which lurked suspicions as fierce as they were unreasonable. And the tic, over which he had by now lost all control, tortured him relentlessly. It was only when he heard the sharp noise of the drawer in Julius's safe closing on the stone that he breathed easily once more.

He smiled, took his great knobbly walking-stick and his hat from his nephew's hands, bade us a very courteous farewell and left, returning the following day for a further discussion of the price of the ruby.

When he had gone, I expressed my surprise at the way he had watched over the stone so fearfully. Julius laughed.

'The old chap has erected three pagodas at enormous expense —they must have cost him tens of thousands—and yet it doesn't seem to have been a bit of use. He can't get away from his past.'

Julius scattered on to the table a handful of the inky cheroots the old man had left us, selected one and lit it.

'He's a big mine-owner and jewel dealer now,' he said, 'but he started his career as a highway bandit. Oh, I don't think he shed any blood—or if he did no one knew. He was content merely to rob solitary travellers. Then he became a miner, when the Ruby Mine Company had the monopoly out here. Everybody stole from them, but he was more expert at it than most people—quite a champion, in fact. Then he became the broker —or really a sort of private henchman—to a big American exporter whom he swindled and diddled in every conceivable way. After that he was able to set up in business on his own account.'

Julius took a luxurious puff at the cheroot which made me want to retch even to look at it.

'He runs his own business, I may say, in a perfectly proper and honest fashion,' he concluded.

The dealer returned the next day at the time arranged. His

own broker took his hat and his walking-stick, gave him a cheroot and lit it for him. I noticed that this young man had the muscles and the tough-looking face of a bodyguard.

On this occasion, however, it was the old Chinese broker who, at a sign from Julius, suddenly assumed the dominant role.

The moment had come when the price of the ruby had to be settled by means of finger work under the scarf. The hunted-eyed old dealer was asking over a hundred rupees, but when Julius's broker did the final vanishing trick with the scarf he let out a great roar of triumph, for the price had come down by half.

Suddenly the old dealer's ravaged face was lit up by an expression of pure and childlike happiness, which gave it extraordinary charm. Was this because he had made a big profit? I wondered. Was he thinking of the next pagoda he was going to build, so that his 'merit' would counterbalance his past sins?

When he had gone, I automatically went to the window to look out after him. But there was another character out there who drove him right out of my mind.

This was a young boy—almost a child—with a very bold and lively look in his eye. He was as poorly dressed as could be, and he stood at the side of the road leaning against the saddle of a very ancient bicycle, all tied together with bits of string and wire. But though he was holding out his hand he wasn't begging. He was showing everyone who went by a little sapphire which sparkled in the palm of his hand.

I called the others to come and look at him.

'I've seen some funny dealers in my time,' laughed Jean, 'but he takes the prize.'

'It'll be a stolen stone,' said Julius, 'from Tchaïpin, I expect, at the other end of the valley. Either the boy has stolen it himself or it's been taken from the mine by one of the coolies, who has asked him to sell it. He's brazening it out very well.'

The youth glanced up at our window with a friendly, mischievous expression on his face.

'I know that child,' said Julius. 'He should go far.'

Just at that moment we saw the Hawaiian-shirted missionary's jeep draw up in front of the sewing-machine shop opposite, which belonged to the only Christian in Mogok.

Before getting out of the car the missionary called the boy, bargained for a few moments and then, laughing heartily and slapping him on the shoulder, he bought the stone.

'As he can't get a game of poker, the padre's going to start gambling with precious stones,' murmured Julius. 'Nice and cool. . . .'

The missionary went into the only Christian shop in the town. The boy stowed the notes away somewhere in his rags and jumped on his cycle. The former bandit, now wealthy and devout, was walking with dignity along the road, leaning on his stick, and followed by his nephew. He looked after the boy rather pensively.

One day, I thought, the little ragamuffin on the shabby old bike would probably have enough sapphires and rubies to be building pagodas too.

10

THE time has now come to draw a fuller portrait of the man who acted as our key to the valley of rubies. Jean's colleague, Julius, opened hearts as well as houses to us, and told us all that lay behind the technicalities of his profession, the customs of the country, the faces of individual men and women. His own life was so deeply rooted in the valley that he was himself one of its most genuine and significant characters.

I have already described his appearance. He was over sixty but unusually young and vigorous for his years. He was short, slightly paunchy, but very square-shouldered and compact. He had astrakhan hair, and large, very attentive eyes set in a full, wide face. His swarthiness seemed to be more than skin-deep. And by some curious process of osmosis, he had acquired something of the serenity of the East.

That was how he looked when I first met him in Paris, and when I saw him again in Mogok. Yet, though the features were all the same, in a different country his whole aspect seemed to have changed. In Europe, Julius might have been any other family man of the *bourgeoisie*. He seemed rather stiff and conventional, a little silent and withdrawn, as though he were depressed by the dreary, inevitable procession of days and weeks. Yet in Mogok there was no trace of any of this. His tie had gone and the old canvas cap with the battered peak crowned his silver curls. Leaning on his thick, thorny walking-stick, he walked with short, brisk steps. When he took his dark glasses off, the eyes that were revealed were shining, as though he were young again. He was breathing more freely, and he never stopped talking. He knew everybody and was at ease everywhere. In fact—he was at home.

Only by unravelling the threads of his strange life can one hope to understand the source of this profound change of personality. I pieced his story together bit by bit from details I picked up at various times—perhaps over a whisky at sundown, or as I sat near some table glittering with sapphires and rubies, or at a Burmese dinner party, or during one of our walks through the valley.

Julius was born in 1892 in the south of Russia, into a family of orthodox Jews. He learnt Russian, Yiddish and Hebrew simultaneously, so that from the cradle he was used to the idea of expressing himself in different idioms. His childhood coincided with the great revolutionary movements and the period of dire poverty which presaged the Russian Revolution itself and the débâcle of the Tsarist régime. Like most other liberal-minded youths of his day, when he was fifteen Julius belonged to a secret society. The members were Jewish socialists, on whose behalf Julius distributed revolutionary leaflets and tried to indoctrinate the workers in the factories. Soon he was wanted by the police—which meant that if he were caught he would be deported to Siberia. He carried forged papers and lived a precarious life, sheltering sometimes with the *moujiks*, sometimes with the Rabbis, sometimes with prostitutes. Finally he escaped from Russia.

In 1909, at the age of sixteen, he arrived in Constantinople. This was one of the most active centres of Zionism, for at that time Palestine belonged to Turkey and to the Red Sultan, Abdul Hamid. Julius joined the movement, and was active in spreading propaganda. But also he had to live, and he was taken on as errand boy to a pearl and diamond broker. He found that he had a taste for these smooth little seeds, and for the sparkling jewels. He began to learn the rudiments of what was to be his own profession.

Then he went to the Lebanon, which at that time was simply another province of the Sublime Porte. He learned English at the American University in Beirut. He was now eighteen years old. Being physically fit and a firm believer in Zionism, he went to Palestine to help in the building of the new land, for these were still the heroic days. Sand dunes rolled over the place where Tel Aviv now stands, with its population of over half a million, and the Israeli colony, all of them pioneers, lived in a few remote hamlets. Julius was among the most enthusiastic of them. Yet, one fine day, he left Palestine.

'I wasn't a saint,' he told me, pulling a characteristically wry face. 'I had my future to think of. I wanted to see the world and earn a bit of money.'

In order to do both these things at the same time he entered the pearl trade. He learnt to know Arabia and the coasts of the

Persian Gulf from Djeddah to the islands of Bahrein, travelling overland on horseback, on mules, on camels, and on foot, and sailing the sea in *feluccas*, in *sambouks*, and in *dhows*.

When he was twenty he arrived in India. At this time Bombay was the biggest pearl-market in the world, and Julius settled there. Then came the First World War. Julius was still a subject of the Tsar, but a fugitive with no passport, and a revolutionary wanted by the Russian police. He heard that the government in St. Petersburg were sending a ship to call at all the British ports to collect all Russian nationals for mobilization.

'Nice and cool,' said Julius. 'I knew what was waiting for me once I went on that voyage.'

What was he to do? How was he to avoid being shipped to the Siberian camps?

It was then that Julius thought of General Knight who was in charge of the province of Bombay. They were both members of the Yacht Club. Everyone knows the Englishman's deep-rooted feeling of loyalty where a relationship of this kind is concerned. And this was India, during what was still the Kipling era.

'Well, my dear boy,' said General Knight, in one of the little rooms at the Yacht Club. 'You're putting me in a damned embarrassing position. I don't want to hand you over to these candle eaters, but really it's my duty. We're their allies. Have you any ideas yourself?'

'Yes,' said Julius. 'I could join the British army.'

'Stout fellow,' said General Knight.

He took Julius into another room where a middle-aged man was reading the paper. He was an officer in the Secret Service, in charge of espionage in the Arab countries. At first he wanted to make Julius pass an exam in the language, but he soon abandoned this idea, when he found that Julius was more learned in it than he was himself.

Thus for Julius there began four years of romantic, fabulous adventure.

Disguised as a poor old Moslem woman, he went first to Bassorah and then to Smyrna on secret intelligence work. Had anyone guessed at the face beneath the ritual veil it would have meant torture for Julius.

Then he had the task of putting handcuffs on the famous

theosophist, Annie Besant, a British subject who so detested the idea of British rule in India that she publicly proclaimed her views:

'I regard it as a blessing every time an Englishman is killed.'

After following a long, tortuous and dangerous trail, he succeeded in tracking down a Greek spy just on the point of fomenting a mutiny in one of the Indian regiments. He also captured a Persian who was in the act of poisoning the water conduits in Bombay.

There was one adventure which he still recalled with excitement, concerning a Russian diplomat named Iswolski, who was posted in Delhi. He was a close relative of the Tsar's former Foreign Minister, and later Russian Ambassador in Paris. A young Russian woman, living in Shanghai, had asked to be allowed to join him in Delhi, and he had given her his fullest support. With this influence behind her, she was granted a visa very speedily, and given the strongest recommendations to the authorities in Bombay, where she had to disembark. They even sent a trusted emissary to meet her at the port. It so happened that this was Julius.

However, the moment he set eyes on the young woman he was warned by some obscure intuition—what you might call the intelligence man's sixth sense—that he should disguise his identity. He used the card of a reporter on the *Times of India*, and introduced himself to the young woman as a journalist. Flattered to think that she was important enough to be interviewed, she let Julius escort her to the suite reserved for her by Iswolski at the Taj Mahal Hotel. While she was in the bathroom, Julius made an expert search of her luggage and stole a photograph of her.

He had no valid reason for any of this, nor for his subsequent activities. He was impelled solely by his strong, though purely instinctive, distrust.

'That evening,' said Julius, 'I called at certain houses which I had been keeping an eye on, and showed the photograph to some of the women there. As you know, brothel-keepers and prostitutes belong to a very close international fraternity, as well organized as any in the world. When they saw the photograph of Iswolski's noble protégée, now installed in the luxury of the Taj Mahal Hotel, one out of every two exclaimed: "Why, that's Mania of Shanghai!" She was an old colleague, you see. Nice and cool . . .'

Here Julius paused to make a few lively and pertinent comments upon the foolishness and gullibility of mankind, and of men in particular, always ready to dress the bird of humble plumage in peacock's feathers, to gratify their own vanity.

When General Knight sent Julius's report to Delhi, and Iswolski was warned as tactfully as possible, the latter flew into a furious rage. It was outrageous, he declared, that the word of a gentleman, a representative of the Tsar, a member of one of the most influential families in Russia, should be set at naught just because of some gossip among policemen and prostitutes.

'Young Iswolski was in perfectly good faith himself,' said Julius, sighing as he resumed his tale. 'You can see how it was. He had met the sweet Mania on his way to Delhi, in a bar in the French quarter of Shanghai. He preferred to think that he had seduced a princess, rather than that he had merely slept with a tart. But for me this was far from the end of the matter.'

General Knight, having received Iswolski's storm by way of the hierarchical grapevine, told Julius in effect that even if she were really Mania of Shanghai there was nothing anyone could do about it when she was vouched for by someone so highly placed. They had no alternative but to resign themselves to granting her a visa for Delhi.

Julius protested. He wasn't any particular champion of morality and he didn't care what the lady was. But he felt sure, for some reason, that her presence in India was a threat to the country's security. He begged his chief to keep her in Bombay for a while, on some innocent formal pretext.

'I can't give you more than three days,' said General Knight.

This left very little time. And Julius needed to make some kind of personal, moral, or psychological test of the lady in order to confirm his apparently unfounded intuition. He went back to the Taj Mahal, still passing himself off as a journalist. She received him cordially. Suddenly he addressed her in fluent Russian, which she naturally would not have expected him to speak.

'You're nothing but a whore and a spy,' he shouted.

She was highly disconcerted. 'No . . . no. Please . . . I beg of you . . .' she stammered.

Then suddenly she gained control of herself, giving an outburst of violent indignation. Julius was a liar and a blackmailer. It was all his fault that she was being kept in Bombay, and she would inform her 'fiancé' in Delhi at once. Julius would soon be arrested and thrown into jail.

'She didn't know how near the mark she was with that last threat,' said Julius. 'I wasn't even a naturalized British subject at that time. If Iswolski had begun to look too closely at my past he could have insisted on the surrender of my humble person and then it would have been nice and cool!'

However, the test had worked. Julius had seen on the face of Mania of Shanghai a clear indication of guilt, which convinced him finally that she was in India on the enemy's behalf. He went to General Knight and pressed for a search of her suite at the hotel.

'All right,' said Knight at last. 'But if you don't find anything you'd better start buying your furs for Siberia.'

And despite a thorough and relentless search, Julius found nothing. Nothing, that is, except a copy of a contract which seemed to him an odd possession for this highfalutin personage on her way to join a wealthy and aristocratic lover. The contract was between Mania and a Greek barber from Bassorah, who had commissioned her to keep him regularly supplied with Arab silver-framed looking-glasses. Then Julius played his last card. He took the document to the decoding experts, and the entire staff worked on it right through the night. By morning it had been decoded. It was about a large-scale traffic in arms, and the final aim was a mutiny among the Indian troops.

'Whenever I remember Mania, I find I need a strong drink,' finished Julius, pouring himself another whisky. 'I've never been so near to the khazouk.'

This, he explained, was the Arab word for a pointed wooden tent peg, and the Sheiks of Hedjaz, Transjordan and Hadramut had a habit of impaling upon these anyone who aroused their displeasure.

★　★　★

In 1918, Julius, who was now a British subject, was demobilized and resumed his profession.

Jean's father, who had by this time established his fabulous pearl empire in Paris, asked Julius to travel for the firm in the Far East. Thus, for many years Julius travelled between India and Borneo, Siam and Burma, Canton and Shanghai.

Between two such trips, he eventually married a charming young English-woman from Bombay, and they had a daughter. Finding that the climate didn't suit them, his wife and daughter finally settled in Paris, and though Julius was very devoted to them he saw them only during his brief visits to Europe. His knowledge of the people and of languages (he was fluent in Arabic, Hindustani and Burmese and also spoke a little Chinese) and also his secret intelligence experience made him indispensable as a specialist in the Far East.

If I were to recount all the adventures Julius has described to me—the ruses he has had to use, the thieves he has tracked down, the fantastic quirks of fate which he has either witnessed, suffered through, or benefited by, I should need a whole book for him alone. The setting would be diverse: the splendid strands of Ceylon, the vast avenues of Calcutta, the paradisial islands of Indonesia, the great river city of Bangkok, the high Burmese jungles, a Shanghai which vanished at the time of the concessions, and the island of Hong Kong. The characters in the book would be wearing the Sikh's turban, the Malayan sarong, the bonze's yellow robe, the European's white dinner jacket, and the Mandarin's skull-cap.

But even if one were to write his memoirs down in exact detail it would be impossible to capture the flavour he gave to them in the telling. An extraordinary mixture of Oriental imperturbability, Biblical wisdom, English humour, Jewish irony and Russian sadness made his stories rich in juice, verve, wit, and his own particular philosophy, which was tinged always with resignation.

Then there was also his wry gift of mimicry, his gentle smile, the expression of disenchantment in his eyes, contrasting with the round jovial face, and the inexhaustible gesticulating of his short arms. He also used some extraordinary expressions of his own.

'Nice and cool' was, as I have shown, his favourite phrase,

and next to this came *'khazouk'*. He often used to say that jewels in their natural state reminded him of Arab women with their veils on—you couldn't tell whether they would turn out to be beautiful or not. When he saw a beautifully cut ruby spoilt by a flaw he would say 'The figure's fine—it's a pity the complexion's no good.' And when someone asked him why jewel dealers always had to be shadowed by a broker, he replied, 'Jehovah himself used a broker called Moses when he sold the Tablets of the Law to the Jews.'

★　★　★

Then came another world war.

At this time Julius was in Burma, but the Japanese invasion forced him to seek refuge in India. His family were still in Paris, and for four years he had no contact with them. It was not until the final collapse of Germany that he was at last able to get a passage and join his wife and daughter in France. Though the main part of the war was finished, the world was not yet at peace. And among the countries where blood still flowed there was one—tiny and misshapen indeed—which Julius regarded as his fatherland. This was Palestine, which as a boy he had helped to till in the old pioneering days.

The Jews were now rising against the British troops.

Julius worked secretly to send armaments to the commandos of Haganah and Irgun.

It so happened that he had a brother much younger than himself, whom he loved as a son. When the boy was very young, Julius arranged for him to be sent to London, where he was educated and grew up. This boy knew no other mother country but Great Britain. A tall, brave, active young man, he distinguished himself in the Near-Eastern campaign. He was in Palestine at the end of the war, where he was made an adjutant and transferred to the military police.

Unlike Julius, he had no special feeling of loyalty or affection for Israel or the rioters. On the contrary, he merely regarded them as terrorists and traitors to the Crown. He behaved towards them according to the dictates of what he felt to be his duty.

One day a police informer—or was it?—told him that the heads of Irgun, who were wanted by the British police, were meeting at a certain specified address. Julius's brother went there. When he opened the door he found the pavilion empty but an infernal machine was set in motion which blew him to pieces.

It may have been Julius himself who supplied the explosive charge which killed his younger brother.

It was not, however, until well after the event that he had to face this appalling question. His brother had been buried for many months before the news of his dramatic death eventually reached Julius, who by this time already lived mainly in Mogok.

This was at the dawn of Burmese independence. Chaos reigned throughout the whole country. It was torn by internal struggles among the different tribes. It was insecure, lawless, without communications. Julius was getting on for sixty. Despite all the dangers he had undergone during his life he always swore that, far from being a hero, he trembled with fear whenever he found himself in a dangerous situation. And he was always afraid, or so he maintained, of certain things, which included disease-carrying lice, mad dogs, which it was forbidden to kill because of the Burmese religion, water defiled by sewage, and, above all, the knives and bullets of the rebels, dacoits, or whatever one liked to call them.

During this troubled period Burma, and especially the valley of Mogok, was plagued by all these. However, the fearful, anxious Julius—and, as a matter of fact, I have myself seen him turn pale with fright on several occasions—went back there every year. Nothing would stop him, neither the interminable and squalid boat journeys up the Irrawaddy, the nights passed in buffalo stables, the aeroplane flights, with mules as companions, nor even the murderous attacks of which he so often saw evidence.

Even now, when order is almost established, the land routes are still threatened and the aeroplane, which lands only sixty miles or so away, still has to be protected by a troop of soldiers armed to the teeth. Twice in the course of the same winter the rebels have made an attack on the town. Julius had heard the whistling of machine-gun bullets which had penetrated the walls of his house.

This is to say nothing of the continual nervous strain imposed by physical conditions of discomfort which would have made many a younger man hesitate. He adapted himself to it, as a veteran soldier in the tropics might do. Up at dawn, scrubbed and polished, shaved almost to the inside skin, he never ceased until night fell to interview people, to value precious stones, or to gather information from a hundred secret channels.

When he visited the mines he always carried a revolver. It wasn't for use against the dacoits, for he maintained that it was highly dangerous to attempt to defend oneself in any encounter with them. His weapon was for use against the many different varieties of snake which swarmed round the holes and little streams of water in the bayon. Julius loathed all reptiles. Also, he was a first-class shot and not at all averse to showing how he could always hit with the first shot the shining, darting head of the snake, as it glided among the stones. This gave him 'face'.

His great popularity in the valley sprang partly from his impeccable integrity, his gruff kindliness, and the fact that if there were no water he would be willing to shave in lemonade. But it sprang still more from his inexhaustible repertoire of Jewish, Arabian, Indian, English, and Russian anecdotes, which he told with unconcealed delight.

Any excuse would do.

'There were once two Rabbis . . .' he would begin, with an innocent air. Or 'Two *moujiks*'. Or 'Two Indian colonels'.

His friends in Mogok, who included everyone who lived there —used to say of him: 'If he gave us a rupee every time he told a story we should now be rich enough to retire.'

But actually they couldn't stop listening to him.

For all these reasons, and despite the way he inveighed continually against the increasing difficulties of his job, the pretentiousness of the Burmese merchants, the treachery of the Indian middle-men, the raids by insurgents, the sloth of his old Shan boy, the drunkenness of his Sikh sweeper, the stupidity of his Chinese laundryman, the caprice of the postal service to Paris —despite, in fact, all the 'nice and cools' and 'khazouks' in the world—it was in the remote, high, primitive valley of Mogok that Julius had discovered what he knew as happiness.

But since nothing could be simple in a twofold life like his, while a vital attachment held him in Mogok, another part of himself could not be torn away from Paris. His wife regarded it as home. His daughter had been brought up there. It was really her true homeland. And Julius, in his Burmese solitude, never ceased to worry about this girl who, a thousand miles away, led a life which had nothing whatsoever in common with his own. She had set her heart on a successful stage career, and Julius would have given the most splendid ruby in the world if it would have helped. But what could he do?

One evening, during our whisky hour, Julius received a letter from his wife, saying that an unusual chance had turned up for their daughter, but that it depended upon her being recommended by someone important. No one in Paris would have thought anything of this, but Julius was a true inhabitant of Mogok.

'A recommendation?' he groaned. 'Why should that have anything to do with it? They're crazy in France.'

Then, succumbing to habit:

'It's just another khazouk.'

Jean put his glass down on the table among the balances, which stood ready for the stones.

'Just a minute, old man,' he said. 'It so happens that there's an old pal of mine—we were parachutists together in Savoy during the occupation—who's not without some influence at the moment.'

'You . . . really . . . would you do that?' stammered Julius.

He had taken off his glasses, revealing a pair of the naïvest, most touching eyes in the world, in a face which was eternally that of the seeker of adventure, and of the *bon bourgeois*.

Jean was already drafting out his cable.

I had already seen many extraordinary things in Mogok, and I was to see many more, but I wonder if that moment, linking as it did Julius's humble Burmese hut with the office of a Minister in the heart of Paris, all for the sake of a tale of the theatre, through the intermediary of the Resistance at its most heroic, and the dangerous quest for rubies, was not, when all was said and done, the most remarkable of them all.

11

THE SOCIAL hierarchy, like everything else in Mogok, was arranged in terms of precious stones.

At the top were the important dealers and mine-holders, the two things generally going together. In this stratum was the wise and gentle grandmother, Daw Hla, and her son Maung Khin Maung; the old tic-ravaged pirate from whom Jean had bought the fine ruby, and Ko Ba Ve who had worked at the rue Lafayette in Paris. Including those we had not yet met, they comprised a mere half-dozen or so.

The top-ranking dealers were paired, so to speak, by the leading buyers, who more or less equalled them in number. These either lived permanently in Mogok, or at least spent most of the year there. They were mainly Indians. There was one Englishman, representing a London lapidary. He was a former employee of the Burma Oil Company, which had pensioned him off because he had been injured by an elephant while at work at the oil wells. Finally, there was Julius.

The third rung of the ladder, in this city built on sapphires and rubies, was occupied by the pweza, or brokers. That is, the important ones, for, like the dealers, they were graded according to their wealth, and ranged from the very rich to the really needy. The leading pweza played so vital and colourful a role in the very specialized machinery of Mogok that it would be impossible to give a really valuable or accurate impression of the way of life, the wheels within wheels of Mogok itself, without stopping for a while to consider this section of its society.

They, too, could be counted without much difficulty. Except for one or two intermediaries, known as 'collectives', because they would accept stones from anyone and offer them to all comers, there were exactly as many brokers as there were buyers. The system would not have worked otherwise: the balance was rigorously maintained, and functioned like some natural law. A buyer, of necessity, had to have his own broker, and the broker would have been betraying the whole principle governing his profession if, in thought, word and deed, he had not reserved all the resources at his disposal for his own particular buyer.

The buyer, who acted as the channel between the rubies of Mogok and the desire which they engendered in the great world outside, was, by definition, a foreigner to the country. He therefore had to have someone to act as an intermediary between the country and himself. And this someone, who was a party to all the plans and complicated manœuvres of his buyer, needed to be a man whose roots went down deeply into the life of the valley, and who was equipped with sensitive antennae which extended in all directions. He had to be shrewd, learned, cunning and diplomatic, with infallible professional judgement, and with an integrity which extended even into his family, for every day fortunes would be deposited with him. Above all, he had to be of unshakeable loyalty, for in the buyer's absence, it was the broker who spoke for him. This would have been inconceivable had not the buyer been absolutely certain that the broker's services belonged to him exclusively.

This was a country of the East, where the leader was traditionally shadowed by a confidant and adviser. The broker was to his buyer what the Grand Vizier was to the Emperor, the stick to the blind man, the pipe to the snake-charmer, the hound to the hunter.

Out of the leading pwezas in Mogok, it was naturally Julius's own whom I knew best. And since it was Julius he worked for, it was inevitable that Kin Chone should have been the most curious of them all.

Kin Chone's father, a subject of the Celestial Empire, but a member of the faith of Islam, had arrived in Upper Burma many years before Mandalay fell into British hands. That period, as distant to us as the Middle Ages, was part of Kin Chone's heritage. Within the Forbidden City of Peking, the Son of Heaven still reigned like a divinity, and Mindon Man, the last of the great Burmese kings, was inflicting his atrocious tortures upon any of the miners of Mogok who tried to outwit his greed.

Kin Chone's father was a humble little pedlar, whose sole fortune was a meagre bale of material which he carried on his shoulder. However, material was in great demand in Mogok, and he had the idea of bartering it for precious stones, instead of selling it in the ordinary way. At first the stones were small, and of poor quality. But in China they were worth a great deal more. He re-sold them at a profit, and was thus able to take back to Upper Burma a better stock than mere cottons. This enabled him to take more highly-priced stones back to China. Thanks to this skilfully contrived business, which brought him increased profits on every trip, the humble pedlar acquired a small fortune, and was able to marry a Burmese woman and raise a family.

Kin Chone, the eldest son, was initiated into the precious stone game at the age of ten. When I met him he was seventy. Thus for more than half a century he had every day been weighing, measuring and scrutinizing sapphires and rubies. And half of this entire period had been devoted exclusively to the service of Julius.

They were an inseparable and truly extraordinary pair. Julius was small and round, while Kin Chone was long and thin. Julius wore a canvas cap, while Kin Chone wore a khaki sun-helmet. Julius never wore a tie; Kin Chone always wore one. Julius could recite whole passages from the Bible in Hebrew, and Kin Chone, who was the leader of the Moslem community in Mogok, could reply with passages of equal length from the Koran, in Arabic. Julius's eyes were hidden by dark glasses, while those of Kin Chone were uncovered. But the very nakedness of his oblique, brilliant, darting eyes concealed their secrets better than any dark glasses could have done. Finally, while there was always a certain solid dignity about Julius's bearing, the broker expended himself unremittingly in bows, grimaces and little monkey smiles.

Yet beneath this servility and cunr' 'g, bequeathed by the old Chinese pedlar to his son, beneath all Kin Chone's little professional tricks, one could detect a deep-rooted kindness, and the essential, worth-while qualities of a man whose long life had been simply and honestly spent. The result was that the puppet very quickly emerged as a human being, with the power to move one to friendship.

He excelled at his profession.

'The old monkey,' remarked Julius affectionately, one day when the broker was there, 'has a unique visual memory. There are one thousand five hundred dealers in Mogok, and he knows every one of them and all their pedigrees. It would be impossible to count the number of precious stones that must have passed through his hands. Yet he can remember all those which were of any value in absolute detail—their shape, their origin, all the adventures that have happened to them. This winter he recognized a sixty-carat sapphire, simply because once, twenty-five years ago, he had seen it in his brother's hand. His brother is no use for anything these days, because opium has got him, but he was one of the best stone-cutters at that time.'

Kin Chone, hearing himself being praised, redoubled his little bows and beat at the air with his hands, to indicate modesty. But on his face there was the happiness of satiated vanity. Yet Jean had only to shake his head doubtfully for all trace of this happiness to vanish at once.

'I wonder,' asked Jean, 'whether you can recite a list of all the jewels in the collection of the former dacoit, U Min Paw.'

Kin Chone gave a small, confident smile of triumph and closed his eyes. He began to intone a long, long litany, strange and sumptuous in content: a song of rubies and sapphires, chanted in a raucous voice. He gave the number of carats of each stone, even of facets; he described the qualities of the cutting, the subtleties of the colour; he dwelt on the beauty of the stars.

'Just look at him,' said Julius. 'He's gone off into a dream.'

'So have I,' said Jean, quietly.

Julius looked at him uneasily a moment, before performing his simultaneous shrugging of shoulders and raising of eyebrows.

'Kin Chone's real talent,' he went on, 'is for chasing up information. One of the first things we have to know is the financial position of each vendor. If he has enough ready money behind him, he'll probably hang on to his price for a long time. But if, on the other hand, he's used all his liquid money—or still more, of course, if he's borrowed—to buy a big stone, or invest in a mine, or throw an expensive party, or satisfy his gambling urge—then we can probably get him by the throat.

'The big money-lender out here, and also the only man who will cash foreign cheques (which is against the law) is a Bengalese, who is the head of the Indian community. Now my broker himself represents the Moslem community. The two of them are naturally in close contact with one another, and naturally in conversation one passes from public matters to private ones. Sometimes the Bengalese will ask Kin Chone to give him an exact valuation of a stone that has been left with him as security. Then, one good turn deserving another, Kin Chone will ask the Bengalese the name of the owner of the stone. And then, on the quiet, I get a pretty good idea of the resources of the dealers.

'But it isn't just a question of the dealers—there are also the buyers, my own competitors. They're nearly all Indians, which fact alone gives them a big start over me. They belong to the East.

'They're much closer to the people here in their whole cast of mind and in their ideas and methods of bargaining. There's a family bond between them. Also, they have an ancient tradition behind them, going back beyond recorded history to the time when their ancestors used to come to Mogok to find rubies for the Maharajahs. Even with the monopoly held by the Burmese kings, and the terrible tortures, they invariably succeeded in taking treasures back with them. The Indian buyers have got this smuggling instinct in their blood. Since the real value of Burmese money is far below the official rating, they secretly bring in Indian rupees and English pounds and change them on the black market. Or, if they can, they deal by cheque, which gives them a purchasing power far beyond anything at my disposal. As the representative of a European firm, I couldn't even dream of carrying on business as they do. So I have to try to find some other method of establishing equality with my competitors, and that's where Kin Chone comes in. His friendship with the Bengalese enables him to discover which Indian has changed any large sum of money into Burmese rupees, or given a large cheque, which will mean that he intends to buy a big stone. Then it's for me or Kin Chone, who knows all the miners and stone-cutters, and naturally, all his fellow-brokers, to find out which stone it is. If I'm interested I rush in at once with my own offer and carry off the deal.'

This extraordinary lesson on Mogok was mainly addressed to me, in my ignorance. But at this point Julius turned to Jean.

'Oh, I meant to warn you, but I haven't had a chance. . . . You know Bapu Lal, who's the craftiest buyer in Bombay, and who has the famous woman broker Ma Kyi as his mistress—well, he was supposed to take the plane this week because his permit has expired. But he's put off his departure because he's worrying about your being here. You might wonder how I know. Well, we've got a doctor here named Abdul Rahim. He's an Indian. He's given his fellow-countryman, Bapu Lal, an obliging medical certificate to say that he ought to stay here longer. And being a Moslem also he's confided the matter in Kin Chone, the head of the community—and my pweza!'

Jean roared with laughter.

'So it's khazouk to Bapu Lal then!'

'That's right,' said Julius. 'A proper khazouk.'

Mention of this word evidently brought to mind a mishap of his own, for he went on suddenly:

'A very long time ago, after the First World War, I was a broker myself in Bombay. But I was on the other side of the fence—I worked for a big dealer, not a buyer. I often used to receive clients on his behalf, and one day I had to see two buyers who came to his office—a pair of very dignified old men from Delhi. Everything about them testified to their importance —their manner, the quality of their clothes, the letters of introduction they brought with them. I had our best stocks brought out to show them. Very serious, with their umbrellas held between their legs, the two old men examined everything rigorously. They were experts, and hard to please. At the most, only one diamond or pearl out of every twenty seemed to suit them. They would put those which interested them to one side, which is the usual practice, sliding the ones they rejected to the other side. We kept on bringing out fresh packets, and the rejected stock was mounting up all the while.

'Suddenly I had a shock. I had a distinct impression that in every batch of rejects—and, mind you, there were some very valuable pearls and diamonds amongst them—there were one or two pieces missing. At first I thought I must be wrong. But then I set myself to count and recount all the stones which they'd rejected. I could only do it by eye, but at this time I had an infallible eye—a broker's eye, in fact. The result was that I found at least thirty pearls and diamonds missing.

'I then asked the venerable pair of buyers if they could explain this mystery. There was a tremendous scene of outraged dignity and besmirched honesty. But I wouldn't give way, and I decided to search them. I'd just had four years in the Secret Service, remember, and I knew how to put a toothcomb over people. It was quite fruitless, however. My two victims submitted with saintly resignation to the indignity, but I found nothing on them.

'At the end of my resources, I threatened to hand them over to the secret police, with whom I still had contact. I was only bluffing, but it worked, because they must have had a pretty edifying police dossier already. One of them glanced quickly at the other, and the other said to me: "If we give them back will you let us go?"

'I gave my word. Then he simply picked up the umbrella which he had leant against the table during the search and turned it upside down. Diamonds and pearls fell out of the hollow sleeve where they'd been dropping them one by one while they swept the rejected stock aside with a lordly gesture. Nice and cool, eh?'

Julius was thoughtful for a moment. Then he turned to Jean.

'But theft isn't the worst that can happen to a broker, is it? Do you remember Daniel?'

'He was a wonderful fellow,' said Jean, 'but he talked too much. He went to Chicago with an absolutely beautiful seven-teen-carat star ruby. The very day he landed, just as he was about to lock it away in the chest in his hotel bedroom, there was a knock on the door. "Telegram," shouted an unidentifiable voice—and when he opened the door he got six bullets in his stomach. . . .'

'However,' said Julius, 'if bad luck ever comes to Kin Chone it won't be through indiscretion. He never stops chattering, but there's method in it—it's all for the sake of saying nothing.'

Some time after this conversation, we went to dinner with Julius's old broker. In his own home he was a different man. There were no more little bows, no grimaces, no little smiles. He wore a skull-cap on his head, and his manner was that of a genial patriarch, surrounded by children and grandchildren. His face, and every movement he made, expressed his quiet, simple pleasure in offering hospitality.

112

The meal was lavishly varied and abundant. Yet the dilapidated walls and the absence of servants suggested poverty. I was
intrigued. Kin Chone had been an important broker for an
important buyer for the past thirty years: he should have been
rich. Or if not, he was very thrifty.

'He's neither one nor the other,' said Julius. 'What he is is
a gambler. Oh, not at cards or mahjong—he gambles with
precious stones.'

Julius's curved lips drew together, sadly and indulgently.

'He's such a gambler,' he went on, 'that once, Kin Chone
himself—my friend and my very own pweza—tried to give me
the khazouk. Among the stones he offered me there kept appear-
ing a ruby with a flaw which made it quite worthless. It was
visible with the naked eye. Kin Chone, however, stubbornly
went on trying to make me buy it. Expert that he was, he
solemnly swore that there was nothing the matter with it. It
was positively childish. Eventually, I asked him why he kept
lying about it. He leapt into the air as if he had been scalded
and threw his sun-helmet on to the floor in the middle of the
office—as you know, no Moslem is supposed to leave his head
uncovered. "May Allah destroy me," he cried, "if I ever utter
a word of falsehood to you!"

'Despite this solemn oath, I still went on refusing the stone.
At last, tormented and in tears, Kin Chone came and confessed.
He had entered into the purchase of the ruby on behalf of a
third party, when the stone was still in its rough state, and full
of promise. Its price then had been high, but, after cutting, the
flaw appeared—and that meant ruin.

'Kin Chone wept. We were old friends. He had rendered me
invaluable services in the past. . . . In short, the matter was
expunged. But ever since that day the notes on the packets
where I hide my stones are no longer in English, or Hindustani, or Burmese—which are all languages Kin Chone can
read.'

'What do you use then?' I asked. 'French?'

'No, it's a bit too well known,' said Julius. 'I use Hebrew.'

He took his glasses off and ran a hand through his silver
astrakhan.

'Yet even with that precaution I've had the khazouk,' he
said. 'Just so that my secrets could be deciphered, there had

to be a Persian broker in Mogok who'd been brought up in Jerusalem.'

He put his glasses back on again. Shoulders and eyebrows went up together.

'A Persian pweza in Jerusalem,' he said. 'Now I ask you—why on earth?'

12

WE HAD only just left behind the last houses in Mogok, but already the main road was no more than a deserted path, dominated by jungle-covered hills.

Ko Ba Ve stopped to indicate a footpath curling round one of these forested slopes.

'The mine's just over there,' he said.

Jean let out a cry and began to run. I followed him, leaving Ko Ba Ve to the company of Julius. They both knew Mogok through and through and were in no hurry. But Jean, who had been kept so busy by the dealers and brokers that he had had scarcely any leisure at all, was irritated, as I was, by every day that passed without bringing us a sight of the ruby mines, and of their fabled, centuries-old treasure, which this high valley, alone in the whole world, had concealed within it.

And here was one of these mines right next to us.

Jean, lighter and quicker-footed than I, disappeared round a bend in the zigzag path. I caught up with him in a sort of miniature creek, at the mouth of a little yellow-coloured stream, where about ten women, their jet black hair and brightly variegated clothes seeming to draw to themselves all the brilliance of the sunshine, were busily engaged in a strange occupation. One by one, they would go and rake the bed of the stream with their cone-shaped straw hats. Then they would squat on their haunches while the water trickled drop by drop through the holes in the straw, plunging their long, thin fingers into the liquid mud and fingering it with infinite care.

I was just about to ask Jean the meaning of this scene, which he was watching, fascinated, when Julius and Ko Ba Ve came into sight. I turned to the latter.

Ko Ba Ve was born in Mogok, and, though he was not yet forty, he was counted among the richest and most influential business men there. Intelligence and authority were written all over his strongly moulded features. He had lived in Paris for his work, and was probably the only man in Upper Burma who could speak French fluently.

'What on earth are these women doing?' I asked.

'You can see,' said Ko Ba Ve. 'They're collecting stones.'

'What kind of stones?'

'Rubies and sapphires. The mine produces both.'

It was Jean's turn to ask questions.

'Which mine?'

'Well, the one I promised to take you to, of course,' said Ko Ba Ve. 'My own mine. We're there.'

He smiled slightly at our amazement.

'Oh, well, you can only see what's left over from the main work here. These women aren't actually employees of mine, but I leave them the waste product in return for a very small rent. They filter through their hats what's left after the end of the real sorting.'

I wanted to wait and see the result of this operation but Jean cried, 'No, afterwards! Let's go and see the real mine.'

It was just a matter of following the course of the stream a bit further, said Ko Ba Ve, so on Jean went, and disappeared from view again.

Once again I was the first to catch up with him. While I was getting my breath back (it was a long, stiff climb) I heard Jean say to himself in a low voice:

'Crazy, isn't it?'

Was he referring to the landscape stretching in such striking beauty all around us? The hills were ridged, as with steps, each ridge densely and wildly overgrown, while at our feet, its steep bed cut into divisions by dams, a red torrent seethed, issuing with force from a kind of white geyser, whose plume shot up against the clear, pale sky. But it is more likely that Jean's incredulous exclamation was inspired by his first contact with reality after all our vague and splendid dreams about the mines of Mogok.

For now we could see the whole mine. The very word seemed unsuitable for this place, worked in broad daylight. This ancient womb of treasure, dressed up in our minds in a thousand fanciful illusions, was now reduced to a narrow, steeply sloping channel, into which a pump squirted water. It was cut up at intervals by wooden structures like steps, serving as elementary filters.

Ko Ba Ve must have recognized the disillusionment upon our faces.

'Yet this is what we call a "modern" mine,' he said. 'Because the water is pumped by electricity. That's all we've got left of the splendours of the Ruby Mine Company. Though in fact, for all their staff and equipment, they didn't do much better than we do.'

'Nice and cool,' muttered Julius.

'The only really important thing,' went on Ko Ba Ve, peacefully, 'is the Mogok bayon—that's the muddy, earthy substance, found nowhere else in the world, where the spinels, rubies, and sapphires lie in their gangue. Apart from that, there must be enough water to wash the bayon. The rest is simply detail.'

He made us climb up to where the plume of water seemed to explode out of the bowels of the earth. From there, in a fairly deep channel, rushed the torrent carrying the red material from which it derived its colour. This red substance was the bayon itself. The furiously rushing stream was arrested momentarily by a series of dams, their sides growing progressively narrower as they went down the slope. Thus the first could hold back only the large stones between its fairly wide-lipped opening, while the last was made so that only the liquid mud could filter through it.

'What more do we need?' smiled Ko Ba Ve. 'A few coolies to mine it . . . very few, if they know the job. And with us it's handed on from father to son.'

There were, in fact, only about half a dozen men. One of them was working the pump, another regulated the force of the water, and the others, up to their waists in the stream, were bending over the dams. They wore conical straw hats, tunics of some floating material, and wide-bottomed trousers. Their faces and clothes were so heavily soaked in the reddish-yellow mud that they all seemed to be made of the same material. A little apart, on some raised ground, stood an old man with a long white moustache and hard, constantly vigilant eyes, who did not carry these hall-marks of the trade. He was the foreman or overseer.

'The coolies are all honest,' said Ko Ba Ve. 'I know them all. But still——'

'When will they be collecting the stones from the dams?' asked Jean.

'At five o'clock in the afternoon,' said Ko Ba Ve. 'At least that's how a modern mine works, because the electric power which works the pump doesn't function any later than that. It's not a recent system. As I told you, it dates from the Ruby Mine Company, and that went bankrupt in 1920.'

'Can we come back at five o'clock?' asked Jean.

'Whenever you like,' said Ko Ba Ve gently, as though to an impetuous child. 'But as often as not we find next to nothing now.'

'Didn't I write and tell you so?' grumbled Julius. 'Didn't I cable you ten times?' He looked pointedly at Jean.

'But why this poverty?' cried Jean.

Julius's shoulders and eyebrows rose as one.

'The mines are exhausted,' he muttered. 'People have been looking for centuries in the same places. They make out that it is only because their fathers were more expert than they are.'

'Yes, they really believe that,' said Ko Ba Ve.

'And what do you think?' I asked.

'Whatever I thought,' he replied, 'there wouldn't be anything I could do about it on my own. To find out the truth one would need geologists, and enormous capital.'

His cheekbones stood out more sharply beneath his amber skin as he tensed his jaws.

'It's up to the government to do all that,' he said. 'And they will. They're the real owners.'

'Quite,' said Julius.

They began to explain the economy of the Mogok mines. As they talked, the column of water still spouted skywards, and the ruby stream roared past us, while the jungle shivered in the wind from the hills.

With the independence of Burma, the bayon, like all the other mineral wealth of the country, had become national property. No one could really own a mine in Mogok, and the term 'owner' was used simply for convenience. Actually, the people engaged in working the mine-beds were only tenants of the State, who had granted them a licence, for which they paid a tax, proportionate to the value of the mine. The value was assessed by the number of coolies required to work it: it came to ten rupees per head a month. In addition, in the 'modern' mines the electric installation and the current cost three thousand rupees, payable to an Englishman who had been a supervisor for the Ruby Mine Company, and who had managed to salvage a few odds and ends from the old equipment.

'Yet poor old Roberts isn't making his fortune,' added Julius. 'Only very few of the mines have mechanical pumps. They don't have the capital. The important "owners", like Maung Khin Maung or Ko Ba Ve, can be counted on the fingers of one hand.'

'How do the others manage?' asked Jean.

'They're satisfied with nature's way,' said Julius. 'They work as they've done since the earliest days, at the places where it's easy to divert the hill springs in order to irrigate the bayon. And when there's no water—well, you just wait for the monsoon.' He shrugged. 'There's something to suit every taste and every purse here,' he went on. 'Do you realize how many holes and trenches are being worked for rubies between Mogok and Tchaïpin? Thirteen hundred—yes, sir!'

'That gives everyone a chance to try their luck,' said Ko Ba Ve. 'With so much variety, you get every kind of combination. People join together to work the beds, and take shares. All according to their resources. There are mines for people of moderate means, and even for the poor. Those are worked by the coolies themselves, three or four or more taking shares, and they have only to pay the tax for themselves.'

'Even so—thirteen hundred mines!' murmured Jean.

'Oh, there could be a lot more,' said Ko Ba Ve. 'We're living on top of rubies in this valley. You've no idea how often they've found bayon when they've been digging the foundations of a house or a pagoda! And water quite close, too. Only the government won't grant any new licences. They're biding their time.'

Julius glanced at his watch.

'We've got an appointment in my office in a quarter of an hour,' he said to Jean.

'That'll give you another five minutes here,' said Ko Ba Ve.

It was only then that I realized how incredibly near we were to the centre of the town.

Before he left, Ko Ba Ve shouted a few instructions in Burmese to the miners, who nodded their mud-caked masks to show that they had understood.

'How much do they earn?' I asked.

'Between five and ten rupees a day,' said Julius.

'What! Is that all?'

It was the first time I had ever seen Ko Ba Ve's expression ruffled by strong feeling.

'The salary doesn't matter very much in their case,' he exclaimed. 'The important thing is that they have a thirty per cent—and with me a forty per cent—interest in everything they find. In actual fact, they're the best paid workers in the world.'

'And do they leave the sale of the stones to you, without any control over it?' asked Jean.

'They trust us,' said Ko Ba Ve vehemently. 'Just as we trust them. If we didn't, life would be impossible under working conditions like these.'

'Besides,' put in Julius, mildly, 'the lapidaries are all pals with the miners. And the brokers aren't exactly clams either, when it comes to discretion. The miners don't really run any risk of the khazouk.'

We had begun to descend the slope, following the course of the stream, which we could watch seething in the successive dams, perhaps leaving rubies and sapphires behind in the bottom. Lower down, near the creek, where the stream came out in a thin, peaceful trickle, the women were still filtering the impoverished bayon through their hats.

One of them, very young and with a charming face, showed us her harvest, laughing with confusion as she did so. It consisted of a handful of small white pebbles with a few blue or red streaks discernible at the bottom.

'That child has at least tripled her stake this evening,' said Julius. 'They pay ten rupees each a day for the right of sifting the waste products.'

A few minutes later we were in the main road of Mogok.

I visited about ten of the thirteen hundred mines. But once I had learnt to recognize the outward indications of a mine never a day passed when I didn't feel myself encircled and haunted by them.

Mines were everywhere. They were in every fold of the landscape, behind every screen of jungle. They were in the sides of the hills, in the shadows of the pagodas, in the clefts of the rocks. They were on the outskirts of the town and right in the centre of it, on the borders of the lake.

Some of them were in keeping with the majestic scenery which surrounded them. But in others the generous, treasure-laden bayon seemed to be emerging from sad and leprous land. There might be up to twenty coolies at some, while at others you would see one or two men on their own, their clothes and faces plastered with dried mud as they worked away at their monotonous, ghostly-looking labour.

It really did give one the feeling of walking upon sapphires and rubies. People went to work in the mines just as market gardeners might go off to their allotments, or factory hands to their benches.

Their everyday attitude, combined with the promiscuous abundance of the mine-beds and the incredibly primitive appearance of some of them, took away the glamour with which I had so generously endowed them in my mind before I came.

Yet, once the first disappointment was over, I became aware of another kind of poetry gradually supplanting my artificial, ready-made notions. There was nothing pre-fabricated about this: it was pure and strong and genuine.

It came to me through the intermediary of that ex-highway robber, now an important jewel dealer, whose tics and haunted eyes I have already described. I have already mentioned also his unaccountable delight when he sold the big ruby to Jean, although he accepted only half the price he had asked. I never discovered whether this was really because he had made a big profit, and was thinking of a new pagoda, or whether it was because it had given him 'face' to deal direct with the great man from Paris.

Whatever the reason, the old pirate, as we called him, couldn't show us enough friendliness. He used to come to Julius's office every morning on a cordial social visit. His nephew, broker, interpreter, bodyguard, was instructed each time to offer us some new delicacy: fruit, sweets, cakes of wild honey, powerful cheroots.

He even made his nephew present us with two very beautiful walking-sticks, each made from a single piece of a thorny tree, a strong, fragrant kind of wood, with gleaming knobbly scars where the branches had been cut off. Jean's was slender, light-coloured and dignified, as befitted a man who could buy rubies. Mine was more like a club. Either because he didn't know Julius's story about my alleged prowess in Buddhism, or because he wasn't taken in by it, the old pirate persisted in treating me—probably because of my bulk—as some kind of combatant whose task was to look after Jean, the big chief. Also, he usually left me to the company of his nephew, as though he were pairing off the two bodyguards.

The society of the nephew wasn't in the least unwelcome, as far as I was concerned. Far from it. Not only did he speak English very well—his uncle had paid for him to have a good education—but a strange, quiet cynicism of his own lent a special flavour to everything he said. I was glad to be sitting next to him on the day when his uncle took us to see one of his own mines.

There were only five jewel dealers in Mogok both wealthy and progressive enough to run their own car. The ex-bandit was one of them, though he contented himself with a very dilapidated jeep driven by his nephew.

We left the town by a route opposite to that which had taken us to Ko Ba Ve's 'modern' mine. The journey was quite short, yet we seemed to come into a completely new country.

As the jeep climbed gradually up a rough hilly path, one could see, beneath vegetation which grew shorter, sparser and more impoverished at every step, the rough, ridged texture of the mineral earth. In profile the hills were rugged, and at times as steeply perpendicular as cliffs. Yet at no point on their surface was the eye held by any sharpness of contour. They were grained and streaked, worn down by erosion till they were like cloth which shows the weft. To look at this surface brought a feeling of weariness: a sense of cosmic age. The dark fissures which, at one time or another, had cleft them at the base, still looked as though they might be harbouring men or beasts from prehistoric times.

The jeep stopped in view of these apertures, but much lower down, because the road had suddenly become nothing more than a path for wild goats.

The old jewel dealer jumped out of the jeep with an agility out of keeping with his wrinkles and his withered skin. Briskly hitching up the longi knotted round his loins so that it completely freed his calves, he proceeded to climb swiftly from rock to rock. Jean leapt after him. I, as usual, followed the nephew.

The latter was showing no haste. Not that he lacked vigour or suppleness. Far from it: all his movements were instinct with both. But I felt him to be one of those unruffled, catlike athletes who never impose any unnecessary effort on their muscles, conserving their litheness until the need arises for one sudden, deadly release of strength.

'Do the mines interest you as much as all that?' he asked me out of the corner of his mouth as we walked on.

'Yes, of course,' I said. 'Don't they interest you?'

'Not in the slightest,' he said, with a sigh. 'The mines are there for the stones and the stones are there for the money, and that's all there is to it.'

'And what's the money there for?'

'Cards and mahjong,' said he, simply.

I recalled the many tales I had heard about the Burmese passion for gambling, which could eat up, perhaps in one evening, the fruits of months and months of desperately hard work.

'What about your uncle?' I asked.

'He's become a great sage now,' said my companion, as though he regretted the fact.

'But what about in his youth?' I persisted.

The old pirate's nephew allowed his enigmatic gaze to rest upon my face for an instant.

'He had other ways of enjoying himself in those days,' he said.

We had now reached the top of the slope. The land stretched unevenly before us, bounded by the towering millennial cliffs, grey and streaky like elephant hide. I combed the landscape in vain for a sign of Jean and the old dealer.

My companion called out in a low voice to a man whom I had failed to distinguish from the rock against which he was leaning, for he had taken on the same colour. His loose jacket, his wide-bottomed trousers, his hands, his cheeks and his forehead were, in fact, all smothered in granulated dust, like stone ash. He wore the usual miner's clothing, but there was something curious and formidable about the speed of his movements, and his eyes, which looked strangely exposed in his grey mask of powder, had the hard, vigilant, concentrated stare of the hired desperado. The coating of dust had obliterated from his face any indication of his age, and I wondered instinctively if he hadn't once served his master in another capacity than that of miner— crouching in the jungle to ambush the solitary traveller or the defenceless mule-driver.

The nephew sat down on a piece of rock, stretched out his legs, and lit one of the pungent black cheroots.

'If you want to re-join your friend, follow that man,' he said.

The coolie was already moving swiftly and silently along the hollow path which followed the shape of the cliff. His bare feet touched the rough, sharp ground. I had travelled after him with difficulty for a few hundred yards when he suddenly folded himself in two, hunched up his shoulders, and vanished, as though the ground had swallowed him.

When I came to the same spot I stooped down and found that there was a very narrow opening cut irregularly into the stone. It led out to a slope, sliding down towards a dark and gloomy hole. As I hesitated, a light was swung backwards and forwards in the darkness and I heard the coolie's harsh voice hail me briefly. I let myself down into the fissure, but, being of far from serpentine slimness myself, I had to grovel about on my knees, grazing my shoulders on the ridges of flint before I finally reached the cave, which was feebly lighted by the coolie's storm lantern. The ceiling was so low that a man of normal height could not stand fully upright, and the walls were so close together that one felt as though one were in a vice.

In the centre gaped a hole, penetrating right into the bowels of the earth, and acting as a channel from which issued a muffled, monotonous noise.

My guide lay down on the ground, and, in order to give as much light as he could, stretched his thin but wiry wrist over the pit, with the lantern hanging from it. An exclamation escaped me before I could suppress it. Was I really expected to entrust my weight to that fragile ladder? It was a mere pole of bamboo, crossed at widely-spaced intervals by steps made of the ends of rushes, and just wide enough to accommodate a bare foot. The whole thing swayed dangerously over the black abyss.

Amour propre alone made me press on.

At the end of this horrible descent stretched a series of small caves, joined to one another either by corridors so narrow that one had to crawl on one's belly, or by mere sticks of bamboo, vibrating all the while and terrifyingly slender, thrown across impenetrable abysses.

In each of these cells, in the pale light of the storm-lanterns, there would be a man, either standing or kneeling, scratching away at the walls and ceiling with an iron claw, scraping off the dark clay, which dropped into a bucket-shaped wicker basket. They were like termites in the depths of hell.

Someone brushed against me. It was the coolie who had led me there. He now picked up the full baskets and carried them through the agonizing tunnels and over the frail subterranean bridges until we came back to the wobbly bamboo pole which led to freedom and fresh air. As we collided, one of the baskets spilled its clay out on to the ground.

He collected it with great care. Then he fixed his hard gaze upon me.

'Bayon,' he said, in a tone of fierce reproach.

Now I understood what the termites had been scratching at in the heart of the hill. It was the special substance of Mogok: the soil which held the jewels.

Jean and the old pirate came up out of the depths of the mine and rejoined me.

'It's wonderful, isn't it?' cried Jean.

I scarcely recognized him. He was smothered from head to foot in mud and ruby dust. I could hardly have looked any different myself. But he went on regardless.

'Just think of it—they've been digging like that for centuries, just like moles. It's all exactly as it's always been. The same tools, the same tunnels, the same footbridges, the same baskets. Nothing has been changed since the time of the first Burmese kings.'

We could still hear the scraping of the iron hooks against the friable walls and the soft rustling noise of the bayon dropping into the wicker baskets.

'We're twenty feet under the ground even here,' went on

Jean. 'But further on the pits are as deep as forty-five feet, and further on still they're as much as fifty-five. You have to go down with the aid of ropes.'

I visualized an endless labyrinth of passages, tunnels, pits and scaffolding, and of narrow, fragile, decrepit underground bridges. I turned to Jean.

'Did you go down there?' I asked.

'No thanks,' he said. 'I've got more regard for my skin. But the old pirate tried for all he was worth to take me. He really is incredible.'

The old man certainly did seem to have re-discovered his youth in some diabolical manner. We could see him in the light of the storm-lantern laughing away with all his wrinkles and tics, his longi still hitched up to mid-thigh. And when it came to climbing up the terrible bamboo pole he did it with the ease and agility of a seaman in the days of sail, shinning up to the yard-arm.

We had scarcely emerged ourselves from the fissure which led to the outside world when the coolie porter came out also, bearing his baskets full of bayon. He emptied one on the right side of the path, which ran between two slopes like a channel, and the other on the left. The two slopes were evidently entirely composed of the ruby earth.

'But where's the water for washing the bayon?' I asked the old pirate's nephew.

'There isn't any,' he said, casual as ever. 'The monsoon brings it. This path is a torrent then. They put dams in it and the water pushes the bayon through.'

I closed my eyes so that I could concentrate on the mental picture called up by his words. I saw rain falling in cataracts, splitting open the sky, drowning the horizon. I saw little yellow men standing in the torrential downpour, searching the mud for bits of precious mineral. . . . When I opened my eyes again I saw the green valley spreading around me as far as the roofs of Mogok.

Jean tapped the bank of bayon.

'Aren't you afraid of theft?' he asked.

'My uncle knows how to pick men,' said the nephew. 'And anyway we aren't still in the days of the Ruby Mine.'

His uncle, who had once enriched himself so effectively by

swindling the Ruby Mine Company, shook his head with one of those vague, tenderly reminiscent smiles which come upon the faces of the aged when they recall the days of their youth and vigour.

'Ruby Mine,' he murmured softly.

The coolie shot out of the ground again with his baskets of bayon.

The nephew lit another cheroot.

'The best coup that was ever made in the Ruby Mine days,' he said, 'happened in these pits. A coolie who was scraping the walls felt a huge piece of rough mineral under the point of his tool. He carefully detached it and found that it was a three-hundred-carat sapphire.'

'Three hundred carats!' cried Jean.

The young man called across to his uncle in Burmese, and the latter noisily confirmed what he had said.

'The miner hid it in a corner of the cave where he was digging,' the young man went on. 'The rough mineral was really too big for him to be able to get it out without being seen. So the following day he cut it in two with a special saw. Then he took each half away separately. Later the two pieces were fitted together.'

Jean suddenly advanced upon the young man.

'Wasn't it your uncle who bought it?' he asked.

'Oh no,' said the nephew. 'He wasn't rich or powerful enough then. The man who bought it died a year ago. His name was U Min Paw.'

At the mention of this name the old pirate's face was wrung by a sudden tic, more violent than ever. But his nephew went on with what he was saying.

'As well as his money, U Min Paw had luck as his middle name. And everyone was afraid of him too, of course. When he died he owned the finest rubies and sapphires in the whole valley.'

'And what's become of all the stones?' asked Jean.

His voice couldn't have been more casual. But the young man's face at once became closed.

'No one knows,' he said carelessly.

I looked at Jean, but it was impossible to catch his eye. He was obviously determined not to arouse any suspicion in our companions. It was not until we were at the end of the path that he spoke again.

'Wasn't there some news from Bangkok in Thailand, about a month ago?' he asked, getting into the jeep. 'Something about a huge sapphire—flawless except for an almost invisible defect in the middle, as though it had been cut in two?'

'Oh, people say all sorts of things,' said the young man.

Thailand—Bangkok—a memory came back to me. It was of the crowded race-course in Bombay, and of the little yellow man with smiling, enigmatic eyes who had come up and had a whispered conversation with Jean.

I turned to my friend.

'That Siamese we met in Bombay was the first link in the chain, wasn't he?'

Jean made no reply. His eyes were fixed on the hill, inside which ants in human form were still scraping and scratching away in the sapphire and ruby caves.

13

IN THE whole of Upper Burma, which was far larger than France in area, there were only seventeen white people.

It hadn't always been like that. Under the British, and especially when the Ruby Mine Company was at the height of its glory, Mogok itself had been teeming with Europeans. All the directors, engineers, and supervisors had lived there with their families, and white adventurers—ex-soldiers and sailors, ex-convicts, ex-bushrangers, and adventure-struck students—had rushed from all over the world towards the ruby-red mirage. And even when their illusions of grandeur, combined with the miners' inherited, invincible art of theft had brought about the ruin of the Ruby Mine Company, there still remained in the country enough British officials, enough army and police officers, foresters, hunters and explorers to keep alive an elegant and intensely active social life.

There were big clubs, bungalows beautifully fitted out for the floating population, fine cottages surrounded with lush velvet lawns for the sahibs, tennis and golf courts, even a polo ground. Such are the outward signs of British occupation, to be found wherever it has lasted for any length of time, from Hong Kong to Uganda.

But in Upper Burma, the war, the Japanese armies, and finally the granting of independence, swept these amenities of a foreign civilization irrevocably away.

Now, there remained, all in all, exactly three English residents in Mogok.

Three old men. Three very strange characters.

★   ★   ★

Roberts was the youngest in years, though he had been in the valley the longest. He was seventy. He had arrived in Mogok at the beginning of the century. Apart from the fact that he came from India, no one knew anything about his antecedents. He was tall, active, and clever, and, despite the wild rumours about the treasures of the valley, he hadn't come to gamble for precious stones like so many of the others. He was employed by the Ruby Mine Company as supervisor in the electrical power station.

The company paid enormous salaries to all their white employees, especially the English ones, and Roberts was able to live like a lord while saving at a rate which he hoped would enable him to finish his days in peace. The company's collapse put an end to such dreams.

Many of the staff left Burma to seek their fortunes or look for security elsewhere. Roberts stayed. He spoke the language of the valley, and he had come to love the people with their peaceful way of life, and the women, with their exquisite colouring. He made a little workshop and did odd jobs in the mines. Even when the Japanese invaded he stayed, hiding in the jungle or in the caves. The people had known him so long that they had adopted him, and also he was by now related to several families by marriage, or through other connections.

At the end of the war, Roberts asked for permission to make use of the remains of the once splendid electric power station of the Ruby Mine Company. Although the Rangoon Government, after such a long period of servitude, was fiercely distrustful of all foreigners, and especially of the English, they conceded this to Roberts, for after all he was more than half naturalized. Besides, how many electricians would have undertaken to repair a forty-year-old plant, with two retreating armies ferociously pursuing one another over the top of it?

Thanks to patience and ingenuity, Roberts had succeeded in getting the engines going again and repairing the circuits. The town owed the fact that it had electric light to his efforts. It was he who supplied the few 'modern' mines in Mogok with electric power to pump the water for washing the bayon during several hours a day.

Roberts's power house stood on the banks of Mogok lake—the Lake of Witches—and it consisted of a sort of enormous shed open to every wind that blew and full of undescribable metal chaos which panted and groaned and wheezed with exhaustion, but worked all the same. Wandering about among the machines there would be a few slit-eyed, hollow-cheeked workmen in greasy rags. It was Roberts alone who brought life to it all. He had red hair streaked with grey, a powerful chest, a face the colour of wine dregs, blood-shot eyes and a voice as harsh and grating as that of his old iron in action. His old Burmese house nearby was like a lair, where he lived the life of a solitary wild boar, never going near anyone. Yet he was regarded with great affection in Mogok.

He gave free light to the pagodas and the Buddhist monasteries.

★ ★ ★

Burke was far and away the oldest of these three Englishmen, who, through the workings of destiny or some strange taste of their own, were spending the closing years of their lives among these wild and splendid mountains. He was nearing his eighty-fifth year. He was firm and upright of carriage, with a light step and bright, lively eyes. It was as though his muscles, through long use, had retained something of the acrobatic suppleness of his distant youth, when he had served on the great silent sailing ships, magic towers of white, which had dipped on the waves of many oceans.

Lashed by the south wind as he balanced aloft on a groaning mast, or hooked between the yards, Burke had voyaged several times round the stormy promontory of Cape Horn and back again.

Then one day, perhaps because he had fallen in love with a girl, or drunk too much rice wine, or merely on an impulse, Burke had deserted. He travelled up the Irrawaddy, roughing it on the flat-bottomed boats which crossed the sank-banks, or steering rafts made out of tree-trunks. Then he worked in the teak lumber camps, where the men shared their daily lives with troops of elephants.

In 1900, at the most torrid time of the year, Burke, overcome with the heat and suffering from fever, decided to give himself a breathing-space. He went to seek a cooler climate at Maymyo, which is to Burma much what Simla is to India, or Dalat to Indo-China—the hill station, or summer capital.

Burke had his meals at the club. One very busy morning when there was not much room, he was obliged to sit opposite to the director-general of the forestry service in Burma. The young man ordered his porridge and fried eggs rather diffidently, but he found his distinguished neighbour very friendly. When the forestry official learned that Burke sold wood he put the simple question between two mouthfuls:

'Would you like a forest?'

'I certainly should,' said Burke. 'I mean I certainly should, sir,' he added, hastily.

'Come and see me in my office,' said the director-general. Then, having finished his breakfast, he rose to his feet.

When Burke joined him in his office, he found a free contract for the concession waiting for him.

But he sighed.

'I've been thinking, sir. I'm afraid I shall have to refuse. A forest isn't any good to me without the elephants for working it. They're very expensive, and I haven't the money.'

'I'll advance you what you need,' said the director-general.

So it was that Burke became the owner of a huge forest of the finest teak between the valley of Mogok and Tabeytchin, which is the port on the Irrawaddy serving the region. He was soon able to pay back the advance, and to amass a considerable fortune.

He married a Burmese woman of good family, and then, with the advance of age, he bought a house near Mogok and retired there.

It was now more than sixty years since he had left his sailing ship at Rangoon.

Some time before my arrival in Mogok, Burke had suggested to Julius that they found a club in Mogok.

'What a good idea,' said Julius. 'It would give a lot of pleasure to our friends in the town. Let's see, as members we could have Maung Khin Maung, for instance . . .'

Burke looked at him severely, cutting him short.

'Natives?' he cried. 'What an idea!'

'Well, who else?' said Julius, nonplussed. 'There are only four of us. . . .'

'Four Englishmen are quite enough to make a club,' said Burke.

Yet it was Burke, the survivor of Cape Horn, whom we had seen on the landing-ground at Momeïk, guiding his old, blind Burmese wife towards the plane for Mandalay. He had been supporting her faltering steps with the greatest care and tenderness, while she took little puffs at her long, white clay pipe.

And then, above all, there was the third Englishman.

★   ★   ★

In front, our house looked out on to the shops and stalls of the main road, but at the back there rose a steep wooded hill. Climbing this, one came first to a beautiful pagoda, all brown and in ruins, then, suddenly, the jungle. Continuing up the slope one came upon a symmetrical hedge, made of carefully clipped bushes, standing there, right in the middle of the wild, virgin growth. The only way through this long, well-grown wall of leaves was through a simple gate on which, despite the fact that some of the letters were rubbed off, one could still see the two words:

'Lonely Spur'

This was the name the owner had given to the house when he had it built in about 1930. He still lived there: a retired Indian army major, aged seventy-five.

I remember that the morning when Julius took us there was particularly hot, and the air was heavy with the wild forest scents. I remember, too, a strange feeling which came upon us all just after we had entered the gate, arresting our progress for a moment. One step more was all that was needed to carry us from one world into another. On one side of the hedge seethed the boundless, untamed savagery of the jungle. On the other, spread out before us, was an enclosed world where everything was orderly, formal, elegant.

The garden made a charming and dignified stairway up the hillside, for it was cut into terrace after terrace of lawns and flower-beds. There were magnificent clumps of tall trees. Vistas, arranged with exquisite precision, led the eye gently towards the mountains, valleys and forests, and the sky.

It was peaceful, luxurious. Yet it was a peace and luxury one could not savour, for there was also a strange feeling of unease, engendered by the total silence.

Such a place seemed to need busy domestic sounds: gardeners laughing, servants coming and going. But amid these formal lawns and flower-beds, along these paths, nothing stirred, and no voices sounded. Only the birds twittered unseen in the privacy of the tree-tops.

'Come on,' said Julius. 'My boy sent word yesterday that we were coming.'

At the end of these embalmed terraces there came into view

one of those rare houses which are immediately gratifying to the eye and to the mind. It was spacious and solid, yet at the same time light and gracefully proportioned. It was made of teak, noble and mellow with age, and belonging to the same family as the forest trees which formed its background: anchored so firmly on the hill, at once decorative and simple, it looked as though it had grown up by one spontaneous impulse.

Then, on the terrace in front of the house, we saw a tall, upright old man, even more astonishing than his surroundings. He was very astonishing indeed, but he produced this effect without any assistance from the extravagant, the fantastic, or even the picturesque. On the contrary, it was the complete absence of any element of that kind, in such a place and in such a climate, which produced so unreal and dreamlike a sensation.

The master of Lonely Spur, the lord of the tamed jungle, wore a tweed sports coat, flannel trousers and a woollen tie, as though he were in Surrey or Kent. He had rosy cheeks and blue eyes. His thinning hair was very carefully parted at the side, and there were yellow nicotine stains on his short grizzled moustache. In short, there stood before us a retired member of the British Indian army—an officer and a gentleman.

His voice was no less typical—brief, firm, but very polite.

'I'm sorry that I wasn't there to meet you sooner,' he said. 'But for a long time now there's been no boy at Lonely Spur to announce my guests.'

He smiled and fingered his moustache.

'Or to do anything else for that matter,' he added.

I could not restrain myself from glancing round at the banks of flowers where no stray weed was to be seen, at the smooth, straight-edged terraces, at the paths which led to the house, all swept and scraped as though for an inspection. The major noticed the glance and smiled again.

'It gives me something to do,' he said, 'and keeps me in form.'

Out of one of the doors shot two little Scotch terriers, charming balls of stiff thick fur, which rolled together at the old man's feet.

'Jimmy left them with me when he went back to the old country,' the major said to Julius.

From the conversation which followed, Jean and I gathered that Jimmy was an Englishman contemporary with our host, who had come from the jade country of Mogaung, passing through Mogok on his way to Rangoon, from where he sailed back to England for good.

After Jimmy, the two men talked of Bob and Jack, and then of Bill and then of Margaret. They dealt, one by one, with each of the fourteen Europeans who lived in Upper Burma, outside Mogok. They lived hundreds of miles apart, separated by inaccessible mountains, bush, virgin forest, or jungle. Yet the abundance and precision of detail made it seem like a conversation about people who all lived in the same village.

Finally the major turned towards Jean and me with his quiet smile, which gently raised the corners of his yellowed moustache.

'You'll have to excuse us,' he said. 'We provincials always like to talk gossip.'

Then he raised his walking-stick, and at a smart military pace, followed by the two little dogs, he led us in the opposite direction from the one we had just come in.

The paths gave place to bushes, the bushes to thickets, the thickets to jungle, and still the major kept on walking.

'I suppose we've come a long way out of your property now?' I inquired.

'Ah, you suppose wrong, young man,' replied the major. 'You're not even in the middle of my property yet.'

His smile seemed amiably to mock himself and the world about him.

'When I bought the hill,' he said, 'my pay was high and prices were low. Yes—there were such times.'

Times, thought I, when polo was played in the valley of Mogok, and when a Burmese presenting himself before a sahib had to bow down until his hands touched the ground. Today the jungle had reclaimed the field where the ponies used to run, and the Burmese were dictating to the sahibs. And no foreigner could own a handful of Burmese soil unless he had lived in Burma for at least twenty years.

The major's train of thought must have been the same as my own.

'The wheel turns for people,' he said lightly. 'But the land doesn't alter, nor does the character of the people who live there.'

His knowledge of the land and of the people proved to be staggering. It was something far beyond learning. In depth and understanding it went right down to the roots. It was fed by sympathy and a profound, organic friendship. It embraced the customs, the language, the history, the legends, the flora and fauna, and even the minerals. Between Upper Burma and this old gentleman there was a sort of marriage of the flesh and the spirit.

As we walked, he pointed out first one flower and then another, calling them by their Burmese names.

'The green lily,' he would say.

'The tiger's moustache.'

'The peacock's tail.'

Or, hearing the chirping and singing of the birds, as one or another of them passed by in front of us, like a flying rainbow, or a fragment of iridescent colour, he would murmur:

'That's the magpie from the Shan country.'

'That's the ruby-breasted robin.'

'That's the sun bird.'

'That's the green fly-catcher.'

He also spoke of the gigantic flower of Palaung Thé, which very few men had ever seen, and the silver-eared birds which were rarer still.

He was familiar with all the tribes of the region. He spoke of the great migrations, which were still going on, from Siam, China, and Tibet. There was one tribe, he said, which had originally come from Assam. King Bodaw Paya, the last of the Burmese conquerors, had brought from there a number of Manipor prisoners who then became slaves to work the ruby mines, and took the name of Maingthas.

He also knew all there was to know about the valley's precious stones. The impenetrable mystery which had always surrounded the history of Mogok before the fifteenth century was just a family secret to him.

'The giant spinel set into the Maltese cross on the British Imperial State Crown, and which was given to the Black Prince by Pedro the Cruel of Spain, must have come from Mogok,' he affirmed.

Or again, changing to another topic, he would settle a point in the history of Upper Burma.

'In spite of what they say,' he declared gravely, 'it isn't strictly true that the first motor-car journey from Mandalay to Mogok was run on whisky as the sole fuel. The driver had petrol to come with. But he was too optimistic, and wrongly supposed that he'd find some more when he got here. It was only for the return journey that he had to fill up with some good Scotch.'

As he talked, we kept on walking, scarcely noticing that we were doing so. Suddenly he had to stop. The shade above us had ended abruptly, and the hill had become a precipice, sloping down to where a huge fault in the rock opened out. It was thick with impenetrable forests, little shining lakes, hills bristling with brilliantly flowering shrubs, sweeping up again majestically towards the mountain chain which formed the horizon.

'As you see,' said the major, mildly, 'nature has fixed my boundaries herself. There are tigers and bears and leopards in that valley.'

His eye swept the splendid landscape where every subtlety of light and shade was so well known.

He pointed his walking-stick towards a slope where a network of deep ravines made the shape of a web.

'That steep hill over there's called Pingau Taung,' he said. 'It means the Hill of the Spider. There's a legend that a giant spider keeps watch there over the biggest ruby in the world.'

Jean looked at the hill thoughtfully.

'I wonder,' he said, talking mainly to himself, 'which would really be the biggest ruby in the world?'

The major made a sharp movement of incredulity.

'What?' he cried. 'You're in the business and you don't know the story of Nga Mauk's ruby—the Royal Ruby! The true story, I may say.'

'No,' said Jean, humbly.

Then, with the wonderful valley before us, we heard a no less wonderful story.

A hundred years ago, in the reign of King Bogye Daw, there lived in Mogok a miner of precious stones who belonged to the Shan tribe. His name was Nga Mauk. He worked at the *ludwin* —that is, at finding the stones under the ground, in the deepest caves and tunnels. He put the bayon in a basket, and then felt it with his specially sensitive fingers, to draw the precious mineral out. When his findings were worth less than a few rupees, payable at that time in pieces of gold bearing the Burmese royal emblem of a peacock, Nga Mauk was glad. Stones considered to be unworthy of the royal treasure-house belonged to him. But all those over this price had to be surrendered to the guard who watched at the entrance to the mine and searched everyone on their way out.

Often, like so many other coolies, Nga Mauk had broken a ruby or sapphire that was too large into several pieces. This ruse had been successful for a long time. Then his luck changed. He was thrown into prison and beaten within an inch of his life. The lesson went home. When he returned to the mine, Nga Mauk swore that he would henceforth behave irreproachably.

Then the great day came.

Generally, when his experienced fingers were testing the bayon in the basket, Nga Mauk would automatically reject, without even glancing at them, any lumps of mineral that seemed excessively large, because he knew from their size alone that they could not contain precious stones. But, on this memorable day, when he came across such a lump, that special sensitivity to jewels with which his fingers were so strangely endowed suddenly made him hesitate. He drew the huge lump out of the basket and examined it by the light of his lamp. His heart stood still. He held in his hand a gigantic piece of rough mineral: he had discovered the biggest ruby of all time.

Never for a moment did Nga Mauk think of stealing this miracle of nature for himself. Only the King—he of the Golden Feet—was worthy of it. Yet at the same time Nga Mauk could not bear to think that the merit—the face—of having discovered such a thing should go to anyone but himself. He decided that he would carry the colossal ruby to the King in person. Perhaps, as well as praise, he might receive from the august presence the Golden Sunshade which was the highest mark of distinction.

That was clearly Nga Mauk's lucky day. He left the mine somewhat earlier than the coolies usually did, and he found the guard asleep at the entrance to the tunnel, overpowered with the heat.

Nga Mauk had decided to keep his activities a secret. But

how could he hide a stroke of luck of such magnitude from his best friends? Nga Mauk had taken some of them into his confidence before he left for the Irrawaddy, planning to sail to Mandalay.

Were his friends as indiscreet as he was himself, or did someone among them succumb to the demons of jealousy and greed? Whatever the answer, it was a fact that a man overtook him on the Irrawaddy and warned the King's officers that a ruby thief was about to arrive in the capital with a very rare stone which he wanted to smuggle into India for sale to one of the maharajahs. The result was, that the moment he reached the landing-stage, Nga Mauk was seized by soldiers and his amazing ruby was wrested from him. After which they took him in turn to the East Gate of the city, then to the South Gate, then to the West Gate, and then to the North Gate, and at each one, stripped to the waist, he was beaten within an inch of his life.

He made his way back to Mogok as best he could and was never heard of again. The man who betrayed him received the Triple Golden Sunshade.

The ruby was given to the most expert stone-cutters in the kingdom.

By the time the major had reached this point in his story Jean was breathing very fast.

'And then what?' he cried.

'When it was cut,' the major went on, 'the ruby, which was pigeon's blood, was the size of a large hen's egg. It was known ever afterwards as the King's Ruby.'

'It's not possible for it to have been as big as that!'

'It's absolutely true,' said the major. 'The three last Burmese kings used to display it with great pride to ambassadors at their court, and to distinguished travellers. And Colonel Slade, an eminent British officer, has described it in his notes. At important ceremonies, Nga Mauk's ruby used to be seen as a pendant sparkling in the ear of the King's favourite elephant.'

Jean's voice was husky.

'What's become of it now?' he asked.

'When our troops took Mandalay in 1885—and it was scarcely much of a feat of arms—there was an indescribable panic. The gates of the palace were thrown open to all comers. The furniture and treasures were all taken away in buffalo carts. Even the dynastic images—the most sacred symbols of all—disappeared. In the chaos the Royal Ruby vanished without trace. One hears all sorts of stories about it. King Thibaw carried it away, hidden in his long hair. One of the guards or servants stole it and managed to convey it to India, where it rests to this day in some prince's fabulous jewel-case. Or some English soldier . . . Only one thing's known for certain about Nga Mauk's fantastic ruby, and that is that no one has ever seen it since.'

The major was silent. He had told his story colourfully, I thought to myself, and with a skill and rhythm which showed him to be a born storyteller.

'Why haven't you ever tried writing about these things?' I asked him.

He looked at me for a moment with mild and melancholy amusement.

'But I have,' he said. 'Quite a number of my books have been published in England.'

He smiled again: the curious, bright, steady smile of his which seemed to be summoned up whenever he thought of his own reversals of fortune.

'That was in days gone by, it's true,' he added. 'I've lost my contacts now. Publishers have forgotten me.'

'Have you got any of your manuscripts?' I asked. 'Unpublished ones?'

'Certainly,' he replied. 'Though I'm not very sure where they are now. Let's go in and see.'

Everyone is subject to the reflexes of his own profession. The major's story had turned my mind towards the written word. It had set Jean's back towards the problem he couldn't solve, and which was now becoming something in the nature of an obsession.

As we walked back to the major's house Jean asked:

'And after the King's Ruby, what are the most famous stones?'

'Well, there was the Peace Ruby, so called because it was found at the end of the First World War,' said the major. 'That was the last really beautiful find made by the Ruby Mine Company, but it didn't stop them from going bust. I've never seen the Peace Ruby: I wasn't in Burma at that time.'

'It weighed forty carats in its rough state and twenty-five when it was cut,' said Julius reverently.

But Jean, usually so avid for details of that kind, didn't seem to hear him.

'And what comes next, Major?' he wanted to know.

'I must admit,' said the major, 'that it's only rubies with legend or history attached to them that count for me. The others —the ones the miners and dealers are concerned about—don't interest me in the slightest.'

'Yes, but all the same,' cried Jean, 'what about U Min Paw's collection, for instance?'

'They say it was remarkable,' said the major, with complete indifference.

'And what about him? Did you know him?'

'Certainly I did,' said the major. 'A little old Burmese. Very clean, very devout, very intelligent. He loved order above everything. That was why, in his heart of hearts, he regretted it when the English left.'

'Nice and cool,' murmured Julius.

Having thus given us his impression of the former highway assassin who became a great jewel dealer, the major began softly to whistle an old regimental march and to accelerate his pace.

The inside of the house—the size and shape of the rooms, the furniture, the sober array of bookcases, the dull gold frames— was all in keeping with the peacefully dignified and spacious façade. Everything was in meticulous order. Not a grain of dust was to be seen on the long row of show pieces. The wood and copper gleamed, and so did the old tribal war drums.

Yet here, just as amid the lawns and flowers of the formal garden, one could sense the pain of solitude and silence.

'This house is under a lucky star,' said the major. 'I found it intact after the war. The Japanese who occupied it had departed from their usual custom and nothing was burnt, or ransacked, or stolen. One has to believe that there are gentlemen everywhere.'

At that point he gave his usual smile.

'The fact that I'm not offering you gin or whisky,' he said lightly, 'isn't out of consideration for your livers. It's the fault of my meagre retirement pension.'

141

He put his monocle into his right eye and went off into another room to look for his manuscripts. The two terriers darted between his long legs. In his absence we were struck afresh by the way every object was clean and polished.

'He lives in the house all alone,' said Julius. 'And does everything himself. A major's retirement pension isn't all that large, and he has to pay tax on it twice—English and Burmese. It means he has to count every cigarette, every cup of tea.'

There were two photographs on the desk. One was of an elderly Burmese woman, with a grave, sweet face. The picture next to it was of a smiling young girl with European features, but showing faint traces of Oriental blood.

'His wife and daughter,' said Julius. 'His wife is dead. His daughter's married and in London, in a very humble sort of job.'

'And what about him?' I asked. 'He's never gone back to England?'

'Once,' said Julius. 'He joined up again during the war and, with the enemy pressing, he had to take part in that atrocious Burmese march through regions of jungle and mountain where no man had ever penetrated before. There were corpses littering the route. The major survived, but he was in very bad shape, and he went back to London to be looked after. It took a long time to get him well. Then, because of his income, he found he could only afford to live in one of those prim and sinister boarding-houses where the life is slowly snuffed out of retired people who live on fixed incomes. He vowed that he would finish his days here.'

I went over to the bookcase. Among some beautifully bound books I discovered several novels with the major's name on them. I can still remember one or two titles: *The Indian Pony*, *Adventures on the Frontier*.

Our host came back. He couldn't put his hand on the manuscripts, but he promised to find them and send me one of them.

'There's no call for them here,' he said. 'When I write, it's an occasional editorial for the only English newspaper in Rangoon. My prose earns me twenty rupees.'

His smile appeared again.

'You can learn to do quite a bit with twenty rupees,' he said.

He invited us to look round his house, accepting our praise.

'Yes, it's beautiful,' he said, simply. 'I built and furnished it, and held on to it, in the face of all the difficulties, for my daughter.'

It was the only time his voice had faltered. But he quickly smiled again and went on lightly:

'You know what girls are. A young man comes along and off they go. Though mine writes very often. But we have these accursed posts.'

He turned to Julius.

'Do you know, I sent to Hong Kong three weeks ago for some anti-distemper vaccine for the little dogs, and I still haven't had a thing.'

Julius looked at me significantly. The old man denied himself everything, but not the little dogs. . . .

As I looked round, I noticed a daguerreotype on the mantel-piece. It was of some highly placed British official in the uniform of a hundred years ago, all decked out with orders.

'That's my great-great-uncle, the head of the senior branch of the family that carries the title,' the major said. 'He's shown there in his uniform as Viceroy of India.'

On the wall next to it there was a very beautiful pastel. It was a charming and graceful portrait of a young woman in a dress with paniers. It was hung in the half-light, which gave a strange, disturbing life of its own to that face from another century.

'She was an ancestress of mine,' said the major. 'She married a French nobleman, M. de Lefebvre, who was killed under Louis the Sixteenth, defending the Tuileries.'

The major went with us as far as the hedge which formed the border to his property, at the side of the road. He stood there, a tall figure, towering between red-flowering bushes, with his tweed sports-coat, his flannel trousers, his plaid tie, and the smile beneath his yellowing moustache.

On a level with his smile was the sign:

Lonely Spur.

14

T H E Burmese valley, which had now become our world, had
two poles. One was Mogok, and the other, which was about
nine miles away, was called Tchaïpin.

They were joined by a rather poor track. But it travelled
through a landscape of hills, defiles, mountains and blazing
jungles, so wide and free, so softly and yet so savagely splendid,
that the lack of haste imposed by the state of the track was in
itself a benefit.

Of the two settlements, Tchaïpin, nearly five thousand feet
high, was easily the higher. It was also the older of the two.
It was there that the bandits, deported by the king in the
fifteenth century, and abandoned in the jungle, had lived in the
trees, and discovered the ruby beds. From the founding of
Tchaïpin dated the only certain known history of the ruby
valley. And when, in distant times, navigators had returned to
Europe singing the praises of Kapelane and its legendary
treasures, it was really the corrupted name of Tchaïpin that
they were glorifying.

Little by little, however, Mogok, where the bayon was more
generous still, had stolen Tchaïpin's sovereignty. But there
were still numerous mines being worked round Tchaïpin, and
it remained famous, above all, for its markets. These were held
at regular intervals: once every five days. We chose one of
these market days when we went to make the acquaintance of
the former ruby capital.

But how can one describe the abundance of rich, exquisite,
rough, intense life that we found in Tchaïpin that morning, or
capture the eternal quality it had? Green hills were massed all
round, heather and myrtle and wild mallow shimmering upon
them. Behind rose a circle of splendid mountains; the high peak
of the Lion, covered with millennial woods; the cone-shaped
steep of Pingau Taung, upon whose sharpest peak there stood
a white, golden-needled pagoda, turned by the distance into a
fascinating toy.

The houses in Tchaïpin, scattered along the sides of gently
sloping roads, and made of teak, looked like crimson or flame-

coloured bushes, for flowers covered their walls and hung down on the roofs.

It was a scene which seemed to slope down in harmonious stages from a sky where the clouds floated as light as caravels. In the midst of it was the market, bursting upon the eye.

Assembled in a huge open space, either in the open or beneath primitive canopies, was a dense crowd, in which gaiety, colour, serenity and dignity were uniquely combined. It was mainly dominated by women who had come down the night before from the mountain villages to sell the produce of their land or of their traditional industries.

There were the women of the Lischaw tribe, with large blue turbans above their severe flat faces, and tunics of the same colour, held at the waist by wicker girdles. There were those from Palaung, with very high silver belts, ankle bracelets and wide necklaces like cresent moons. There were delicately made Burmese and Chinese women, wrapped in dark or brightly patterned longis, and sheltering under transparent sunshades. There were Maingthas peasant women in heavy trousers with leather leggings. There were Panthay, the shawls round their heads hanging right down to their waists, and Shan women with cone-shaped wicker hats. There were the Gurkhas, with little ornaments of fine gold in their noses, sitting with their legs crossed, as still, straight and secret as idols.

The women were all surrounded by the baskets containing their wares. These were woven with exquisite artistry and ranged through every colour, from burnt corn to old ivory, and through every dimension, from those of giant size, piled with firewood, to those like beautiful little cylinders, the scarlet of berries gleaming through the diagonal holes in the wicker.

Not once did the women cry or call out as they hawked healing herbs, flowers for embalming, tree-bark which, after one boiling, would preserve the lustre of shiny black hair, tender bamboo shoots, sandalwood and ginger.

The produce looked like offerings, for it was set off by thick, brilliant green leaves, knotted, folded, and spread out with great skill.

Round about the market, through the streets and squares and sometimes in the alleyways of the market itself, neighed and pranced slender-hooved little horses with long fleecy manes and strange saddles on their backs. They were mountain ponies which came from the slopes of Tibet.

The sun gleamed on the merchandise, on the materials and fruit, on the baroque ornaments, on the flowering shrubs of the jungle and the needles of the pagodas. A light breeze brought with it the scents of the mountains.

I had memories of many splendid markets, from Southern Morocco to darkest Africa. I had seen the markets of Zanzibar and of Bahia, of Arabia and India. But I had seen none of so subtle and delicate an appeal to the senses—no crowd so clean and orderly, so refined and dignified of face, no setting so majestic, as these of Tchaïpin market in Upper Burma. This was the Orient entire, profound, wise, authentic, epitomized by its ordinary folk—the Orient of the silk road, of Marco Polo, of the peaceful light of Buddhism.

And to complete it, amid the rows of fruit and vegetables, materials and herbs, there was, quite naturally, a row of rubies.

This gallery of beaten earth, open to the fresh air and protected solely by a rough, light roof supported by wooden pillars, was the only place where men predominated. There were agents on the look-out, miners with finds they had made in the mine-beds in the surrounding jungle, brokers, small dealers and important ones, and curious onlookers of all ages.

The stones, some in their rough state, others cut, lay on copper trays, the sun playing dazzlingly upon them, just as, on either side, it played on the mangoes and tomatoes.

Amongst all the people weighing and scrutinizing them there were, of course, all our friends from Mogok. Julius was there, with his inseparable companion the Chinese broker, so were Maung Khin Maung, Ko Ba Ve, once of the rue Lafayette, and the old pirate followed by his nephew.

It was, however, an unfamiliar face which attracted my attention that day. It belonged to an inhabitant of Tchaïpin. He too was a precious stone dealer, with mines which he worked. But he was quite unlike the other dealers. In the first place he was notable for his broad shoulders and large stature, uncommon among his race. His face was also unusual. He had a strong prominent nose, ironic eyes which scarcely slanted, and a high forehead, suggesting intelligence, resolution, and pride. He carried himself like a leader.

146

According to what Julius told me, there was nothing striking about his origin. He had started simply as a miner in the mountains overlooking Tchaïpin, and he owed his fortune to patient work, simple and sober habits, and a keen instinct for precious stones. But the way he had enriched himself was not the most striking thing about his life: this was his proud and courageous warrior spirit, which had found an outlet in underground struggle.

Although, under the British occupation, the Burmese had accepted the yoke as something inevitable, U Hlaing Shwe had refused to submit. One day he was summoned before the high official in charge of the region, but he replied that he would only attend when he received a written command. The command took the form of a warrant for his arrest, presented by armed police. They brought U Hlaing Shwe before the British Resident. There was a law at the time, possibly not written but strictly observed, that any Burmese, however aged, or however noble his origin, must, when brought before a sahib representing the King of England, bow down before him and touch the ground with his hands. U Hlaing Shwe was only a young man at the time, and little better than a coolie. Nevertheless, he refused to bend his tall frame a single inch, looking the British official squarely in the eye. He was thrown into prison. When he came out, he installed a secret printing press at his home and printed revolutionary pamphlets which were distributed throughout the region by trusted comrades. He also formed a band of rebels.

When war came and the Japanese occupied Burma, U Hlaing Shwe supported them as long as they helped to get rid of the British. Then he turned against the new oppressors. Even the liberation of his country and the declaration of independence seemed to bring no peace to this strange man, possessed by a demon of revolt.

He spoke no language but his own, yet his political knowledge was considerable. He had studied in Burmese the works of the great sociological writers, Karl Marx above all. He was said to be in constant touch with the Communist insurgents fighting in the surrounding jungle and mountain regions. Some contended that he supported them with money and information, others went so far as to suggest that he was their leader.

His house was large but even barer than the others we had visited. It had an austere, even haughtily severe atmosphere. As his wife was kept in Mandalay, where she ran her own oil works, one of his daughters was acting as mistress of the house. She was a beautiful girl, tall and well made. Her skin was light, scarcely amber and wonderfully smooth. In her cheeks were the roses of youth nurtured on the mountain air. As she spoke English, it was she who handled her father's business dealings with foreign merchants.

While she offered us coffee, cigarettes, and honey cakes, she talked to Julius and Jean in a way which showed her to be as knowledgeable as they were about the number of carats, the quality of the stones, and their value in rupees.

But as for U Hlaing Shwe himself, in this too he was unlike all the other dealers, for the business seemed to hold no interest for him at all. A tall, powerful figure, with a coarse, dark woollen Balaclava helmet round his head, he stood apart at the window, staring with hard, steady eyes into the distance. There was nothing in his attitude to give any hint of a rather strange incident which happened shortly afterwards.

Having finished their conversation with the daughter, Jean and Julius went up to U Hlaing Shwe to take their leave. The window which framed his sturdy body was free from glass, like all the others in this region, and it looked out upon a hill covered with fine houses surrounded by gardens. This would have been as charming a view as any in Tchaïpin had it not been for a sort of ugly great wound in the middle: a ruin consisting of little more than blackened, mutilated stumps of timber.

Quite automatically I turned to U Hlaing Shwe's daughter: 'So you've had a fire near here recently?'

The girl darted a furtive glance at her father, but he didn't react. I had spoken in English, and he hadn't understood.

'Yes,' she answered swiftly. 'A year ago.'

'An accident?'

She seemed not to have heard me. It was then that Julius spoke, this time to Jean in French.

'Don't ask any more questions. They don't like talking about that business.'

'Why not?'

'It's a strange story,' whispered Julius. 'One fine night unknown people set fire to the house and the people living in it were burned. All the precious stones disappeared.'

Jean looked fixedly at Julius and asked him deliberately:

'You're speaking of the treasure that was brought from Mogok to Tchaïpin? The treasure of U Min Paw?'

Julius's plump face immediately grew tense.

'I've told you,' he said, 'don't . . .'

He had no time to finish. Our host had also heard the name of the famous dacoit. Keeping his steady, arrogant gaze fixed on us, he began to speak in an authoritative tone, while his daughter translated.

'My father thinks he has guessed what we were talking about,' she said, 'and he would like to make the matter clear.'

At that moment the haughty voice was full of splendid scorn, and his daughter's flexible tones ran together with it in counterpoint.

'My father regards Min Paw as a disreputable character.' (I noticed the omission of the respectful prefix 'U'.) 'He killed members of his own race in order to enrich himself, and then, to make himself richer still, he worked with the British oppressors of his people.'

For a moment the haughty voice was silent, then it suddenly began again, speaking in tones of passionate conviction.

'There are a great many stories about Min Paw's death,' the girl went on, 'and many others about the attack on his house, the ashes of which you can see there. My father is not concerned with this, nor with what's become of the precious stones. But he wishes to emphasize that the true insurgents have no part in aggression and arson. They are pure in their intentions. When they need money or arms to support their cause they know where to come.'

U Hlaing Shwe, still outlined against the windows, spoke again briefly.

'These ruins,' said the girl, 'were made by ordinary criminals, or worse.'

There was a long silence in the huge empty room.

Then Jean spoke to Julius in a low voice.

'What do you gather from all that?'

But Julius quickly shook his head as though to rid himself of a troublesome wasp and hurried us out.

We had scarcely left U Hlaing Shwe's house before Julius gave his habitual sign of emotion by taking off his dark glasses.

'Really, you seem to be taking a great interest in the story of U Min Paw,' he said to Jean.

'Well, wasn't it a fantastic collection of rubies?' replied Jean. 'A maharajah's treasure? A museum collection? Wasn't it you who told me about it in the first place?'

'But that was in Paris,' groaned Julius.

He thrust his fingers to the roots of the grey astrakhan showing under his old canvas cap.

'For the love of God, don't meddle in the business here!' he cried. 'Don't ask me why, because I don't know. But I know the country. The affair has got something unhealthy about it!'

At that moment we passed in front of the bare, burnt patch left by the fire. Jean stopped to look at the ruins.

'Come on, come on,' cried Julius nervously. 'We're already late for Maung Khin Maung.'

This was quite true. Maung Khin Maung, our best friend in Mogok, was waiting for us at Tchaïpin market to take us back home.

The activity of the market was diminishing as the day drew to a close. The Lischaw, Palaung, Shan and Gurkha saleswomen had begun to take up their beautiful baskets, now empty. Men in blue tunics, their heavy hair braided, were putting pack saddles on the little Tibetan horses. The people were getting ready to go to their mountain huts. Five days later they would be back again to hold another market at Tchaïpin, according to their traditional cycle, handed on from generation to generation.

Maung Khin Maung welcomed us with his accustomed courtesy, and with that faint, gentle half-smile which gave such charm to his carved ivory countenance.

He listened thoughtfully to our account of the visit to U Hlaing Shwe. Then he said quietly:

'Yes, that's a man who makes you think—an enemy of the rich who's so rich himself.'

Jean spoke of the burned house and the vanished treasure.

Instead of answering, Maung Khin Maung looked up at the position of the sun in the sky, where a few peaceful clouds still sailed.

'We've got plenty of time to get back to Mogok before

dark,' he said. 'Would you like to have a look round these parts?'

His car wasn't far off. Against one of the wheels there squatted a very small and serious yellow-skinned boy, with a man's felt hat much too large for him shoved on the back of his head. He was playing dice with Maung Khin Maung's chauffeur.

Soon the houses of Tchaïpin were behind us, and we were back in the jungle. Here it seemed more vigorous, more violent than I had ever known it. Heather and mallow were bright on the slopes; thick woods crowned the peaks. Perhaps it was the mystery of these high places, the memory of the deported brigands who had founded Tchaïpin, the fact that tigers stalked the cattle in the vicinity, or the tales we had heard of the insurgents—whatever the reason, there was certainly a feeling of danger in the air. We had come to the frontier of adventure —of the world where anything could happen at any moment.

Suddenly, round a bend in the road, we saw a long, deep ravine full of thick dense vegetation, which made it look like the bed of a large river. It was then that I closed my eyes in order to dispel the delusions of mirage, though I knew perfectly well that at such a height and amid so much verdure the light couldn't be playing tricks.

How could I help but believe that I was the victim of an hallucination when, upon the imitation river formed by the valley and its undulating vegetation, there appeared the floating shape of a strange ship? It had masts which appeared to be bending in the breeze, and rigging which was perpetually moving. I could see tiny human silhouettes working along the ropes stretched against the sky. Only sails were lacking. It resembled in shape the *dahahieh* of the Nile, and by a trick of perspective it looked as if it were being rowed towards us.

Having opened and shut my eyes several times and ascertained that it was still there, and still the same as when I first noticed it, I hesitated a moment and then asked Maung Khin Maung, who was sitting next to the chauffeur, if he could see what I saw.

'Certainly,' he said gently. 'Only in my case I already know that it has to do with one of the mines.'

I turned to Julius who was sitting beside me.

'It even belongs to that fanatic U Hlaing Shwe,' he muttered.

151

After that I concentrated all my attention on trying to capture the exact moment of time when the extraordinary ship would connect itself with dry land and turn into a perfectly commonplace and ordinary piece of mining equipment. But, despite my efforts, this proved impossible. Suddenly, with no apparent transition, the ravine ceased to flow by like a river, and the fantastic arrangement of masts and rigging became detached from it, and rooted in soft yellow soil. But this did not dispel the feeling of fantasy: it was simply that the nature of the strangeness had changed. The way it remained detached gave the machinery a light air-borne quality which I still found astonishing.

It consisted of two high, graceful masts, the colour of honey, rearing up like spikes. Near the top a still thinner shaft crossed them through a groove. At one end of the shaft a bucket-shaped basket was suspended, full of gravel. This acted as a balance. At the other side, on the end of a fine wire, another basket was lowered into a hole of the precious bayon, and came up full. The men operating this primitive hoisting gear had to move about along spindly foot-bridges, narrower than the soles of their feet. In wide mud-caked garments, with pointed hats of golden straw upon their heads, they moved backwards and forwards on these shivering bridges, balancing surprisingly, like tight-rope walkers.

The masts, the bridges and even the pumps which drew the water for washing the bayon, were made of bamboo, one of the lightest and most ethereally elegant of materials. No exquisite old Chinese engraving could have been subtler or more gracefully outlined than this tracery of stalks against the Burmese sky, with the dream-like miners on it, looking now like acrobats, now like fishermen casting their lines from heaven to hook up rubies and sapphires.

All this took place in the deep silence of the country, broken only by the creaking of the bamboo stalks as they rubbed against the shafts. In the distance we could see zebu grazing in the jungle clearings, and iridescent clouds were gliding round the crest of the Lion.

Jean, as responsive as I was to the beauty of the scene, was none the less spurred on by the demands of his profession and by his own impatient nature, and he went off to see what the day's takings in precious stones had been. He came back very quickly: the dams had kept back nothing of any value.

He had often been similarly disappointed.

'But good God,' he cried, addressing Maung Khin Maung, 'is it possible ever to see them find anything?'

On Maung Khin Maung's face, so wise, despite its air of youth and fragility, there appeared that charmingly quiet and indulgent smile with which he favoured any exhibition of lack of control on our part.

'People who make their livings by the mines must do so,' he replied gently.

For a moment he gazed up at the little yellow men on their insecure perch, drawing up the bayon or squirting the water through the hollow bamboo stalks.

'When I was a little boy,' he said, 'these mines didn't belong to U Hlaing Shwe: he wasn't so well off then, because the British kept putting him in prison for his revolutionary activities. They belonged to one of my uncles. One day I came here with his son, a boy of my own age who went to the same school in Mogok. My uncle was annoyed because he felt that his son didn't come to see him often enough and was causing him to lose face. He began to scold the boy very angrily. They were standing by that pump over there. I didn't want my cousin to think that I was standing by while his father told him off so I went away by the stream that washes the bayon. Suddenly one of the coolies let out a tremendous howl and began to wave his arms about as though he'd gone mad. Then all the others came rushing up, so suddenly that I was very nearly trampled underfoot. I was quite small at the time, and rather frightened. I thought they were quarrelling. I called my uncle, who was still scolding his son, and he rushed up too. Then the coolie opened his right hand and showed a magnificent rough ruby. Everybody began to sing and jump for joy, my uncle, who was usually very serious, leaping about more than anyone. He quite forgot that he'd been annoyed. They had a big feast afterwards, and I came in for the best of everything. My uncle thought I'd brought him luck.'

'How many carats was it when it was cut?' asked Jean.

'Eighteen, and pigeon's blood,' said Maung Khin Maung, reverently.

'It was sold to Chota Lal, the Gujerati merchant,' sighed Julius.

The three men were silent for a moment. One could hear the creaking of the bamboo hoisting gear and the sound of the bayon falling into the baskets.

'I remember another find,' went on Maung Khin Maung. 'I was still quite young, and had only just finished as a student, though I hadn't yet started my proper career as a dealer. I went into an underground mine in the neighbourhood of Mogok, and I saw a coolie putting a very beautiful sapphire into one of the bamboo containers. He had scraped it straight out of one of the walls of the tunnel. I gave an exclamation and three men immediately clapped their hands over my mouth. And they gave me ten rupees to say nothing about the discovery. That was the first money I ever earned through a precious stone.'

'But why did they want it kept secret?' I asked.

Jean shrugged his shoulders.

'Professional habit,' he said. 'You never know what your competitors are saying, or what the brokers are inventing, or what the tax officials are thinking.'

'Or perhaps the owner wasn't there,' said Julius. 'And the miners were being discreet out of consideration for him.'

Maung Khin Maung, his silent laugh on his face, turned to me.

'There's nothing your friends don't know about the business,' he said.

He glanced up at the sun.

'If it suits you all right,' he went on, 'we could go now. There's something else I'd like to show you.'

When the car stopped again it was at the foot of a mountain, in front of the entrance of an enormous tunnel which obviously owed nothing at all to the hand of man.

'I won't take you inside,' said Maung Khin Maung, in a voice which showed him to be in some way moved. 'It would take days and days, and even then you would only have gone half the way. I don't know if there's a miner alive, even among the very oldest, who knows the whole of the underground caves where this crevice leads. The whole mountain is hollow. They've been digging in it for centuries. The ruby miners have added hundreds of passages and cells and openings to the natural caves and grottoes. They lead in all directions and are at all levels, from the side or back of every dark abyss or crevice. Even from the place where the bones of the prehistoric beasts are resting: the vault of the Dead Giant Elephants.'

Maung Khin Maung inclined his head towards the entrance to the labyrinth, as though listening to a voice which he alone could hear.

'You couldn't find a safer hiding-place,' he went on. 'I hid there with all my family during the cruellest months of the Japanese occupation. In the past, whenever there was a war or riots, or an epidemic, or a big purge by the kings of Mandalay, our ancestors used to come and shelter in the Hollow Mountain.'

'And today, of course,' said Julius in a low voice, 'the insurgents . . .'

'Maybe,' said Maung Khin Maung, but his face was quite expressionless.

At that moment it happened that my gaze, which had been fixed on the entrance to the tunnel, was caught by a small metal object half hidden by the grass, but gleaming dully in the slanting rays of the sun. I took it up.

It proved to be a very ordinary, valueless ring. But there was a seal on it which I mechanically began to polish. Some Burmese letters appeared.

'Someone's lost his official ring,' said Maung Khin Maung.

I remembered how I had seen Julius in his office, sealing packets of precious stones with his ring.

Julius himself, who could read Burmese writing, was engaged in deciphering the letters on my find.

Suddenly he took off his glasses, put the ring back in my hand and murmured:

'Nice and cool . . . it's U Min Paw's name.'

Despite his self-control, Maung Khin Maung started. His slanting eyes darted towards the ring.

'Well?' said Jean.

'It's quite true,' said Maung Khin Maung, reluctantly.

'But then . . . doesn't it mean . . .' stammered Jean.

He had no need to say any more, for his train of thought was that which we were all following at that moment. Men had attacked and burnt down the house in Tchaïpin where the

155

daughter of a former bandit had hidden his treasure. The magnificent collection of rubies and sapphires had all disappeared. And here, either lost or thrown away, was the seal of the famous dacoit, turning up in a place which for centuries had been used as a hiding-place.

I heard myself thinking aloud.

'They spent the first night in the Hollow Mountain. With their invaluable loot.'

'Maybe,' said Maung Khin Maung.

His voice betrayed nothing, and there was no expression on his face beyond its usual amiability, bent now towards making us start the return journey.

That evening was to yield yet another discovery.

As the car went slowly forward on a road covered with bogs and bordered by high mountain bushes, a great stone head reared up suddenly from the tangled vegetation. It had so striking a character that, despite the lateness of the hour, I persuaded Maung Khin Maung to stop for a moment.

My insistence was more than justified. I owe to it one of the most overwhelming sights a man could see on a deserted road.

It was an image of Buddha, with a face which caused the leaves and thorns and claws of the jungle to retreat into the distance. But this was not one of the classic idols, made of marble or gold, all with the same brow and the same smile, that I had already seen reproduced *ad infinitum* in so many sanctuaries. This was an old, old image, darkened and engrained by time. Abandoned in the middle of the bush, to wind, monsoon, sun and enclosing trees, it belonged now to the elements themselves. From this union with them, from its contact with life at its source, the bust had taken on a character of its own that was both sublime and disturbing. No doubt, somewhere behind the folded lid something of the ancient mystical serenity still lingered, but time and rough weather had hollowed out the cheeks, sharpened the ears, and turned the august smile on the broken lips into a terrifying laugh. I wondered if it was indeed Buddha or not some Faun who now animated this stone being, which seemed both to subdue and to be subdued by the surrounding jungle.

A little further on there stood one of the loveliest pagodas I had seen. It had neither cupola nor golden needle. Like the statue, it was very old, in ruins and darkened to the same mellow shade of brown.

Maung Khin Maung spoke in a thoughtful tone.

'Our ancestors dedicated this temple and statue to the presiding spirit of the mines,' he said. 'They used to come here to pray for precious stones. This spot was chosen because the earth here is very rich in rubies. But they would never dig the bayon round the pagoda. Even the Ruby Mine at the height of its power couldn't induce them to sell this piece of land, despite the most violent threats and the most generous promises of money. They preferred to leave it to the grass and brush.'

As we made our way back, the faun-like smile of the jungle Buddha seemed to follow us.

I noticed also that I had unconsciously slipped upon my finger the dull metal ring which bore the name of U Min Paw.

15

ON THE way from Mogok to Tchaïpin, just ahead of Mogok but still visible from the town, a road on the left-hand side ran off into the steep forested slopes. Where it branched there was a sort of settlement, consisting of ten or so houses, very widely spaced. A shed adjoined one of them, full to the ceiling with huge sacks of rice.

This belonged to the Indian Gopal Singh, a Sikh. As their custom demands, he wore a full beard and a large turban. He was well above the average in height and strong enough to lift with ease sacks which would have been too heavy for two ordinarily sturdy men. The eyes which shone in his hairy face were lively and very steady.

Although a foreigner, Gopal Singh was among those who had acquired most 'face' in Mogok. His commercial acumen had enabled him to develop the little rice business started by his father, who was no more than a poor pedlar, until he had become the biggest dealer in the district in its staple food. To it he had added a prosperous haulage business. But his reputation was not due to his wealth, considerable though it was. It derived from the fame he had won fighting the British in India, first in Chandra Bos's legion of Indian rebels, who were armed by the Japanese, and later with the Burmese guerrillas. Because of this, he had the rare privilege of keeping his own partisan's rifle and ammunition in his house.

When Maung Khin Maung brought us back from Tchaïpin, he left us at the door of Gopal Singh's house. There were four of us: Jean, Julius, his old broker Kin Chone, and myself.

Gopal Singh was, in fact, a great friend of Julius, and he had made us promise solemnly that we wouldn't leave Mogok without visiting him. As we were soon to leave, the visit had been arranged for that evening.

Gopal Singh welcomed us with dignity, a massive, almost brutal figure with his deep barrel-like chest, thick shining black beard, stevedore's shoulders and enormous turban. When the first greetings were over, he said to Julius:

'I've got a guest staying with me who arrived yesterday.

You won't know him. He's a Tibetan scholar. He cured me with herbs once during the war, when I was on the coast of Assam and dying of fever from a poisoned wound.' For Jean's and my benefit he added: 'He speaks excellent English.'

The room where Gopal Singh received us was large and furnished much more amply than those of the Burmese, with Indian idols watching over it all. Sitting there on his crossed legs, as on a pedestal, was a man of indefinable age, with his head shaved after the manner of the bonzes, a very flat pale yellow face and expressionless eyes so narrow that they were hardly visible at all. His European clothes only emphasized his wholly Mongol aspect.

He was drinking very thin tea with great echoing gulps. Gopal Singh and Kin Chone also drank tea, while whisky was served to us, the three Europeans.

Julius downed his first glass very quickly.

'It's good to find oneself safe and sound,' he said. 'I don't like that last defile a bit . . . it was dark there already.'

Jean, who was made happy by only one glass of alcohol, slapped Gopal Singh on one of his iron-hard thighs.

'Old father Julius and his phantoms! Isn't he absurd?' he cried.

But our host's face, generally cheerful and lively, had become very grave.

'I've seen those phantoms myself,' he said. 'And more than once, too.'

He shook his wild black beard and went on:

'The first encounter was a year ago when I was taking some goods and passengers to the Irrawaddy port of Tabeytchin, in a lorry. We were driving through flat jungle-covered country. All of a sudden there was an explosion . . . I thought a tyre had burst. But then a burst of shot whistled past me. It was a sound I recognized at once—I've seen so much of war. I flattened myself out on the road. Then I saw two men in the bushes with Sten guns. And it was me they were aiming at.'

'You hadn't brought your gun?'

'No. And it was lucky for me I hadn't, because I should have been finished otherwise. It's arms that they're mainly after. As it was, they'd mistaken me for a soldier or policeman. I'd made the mistake of dressing myself in khaki.'

'Khaki is absolutely asking for the khazouk,' said Julius to us.
'I warned you about that when you first arrived.'

'I cried out with all the strength in my lungs that I was just
a simple Sikh merchant, and the insurgents believed me because
of my beard and turban. They let us go after stripping us of our
clothes and everything we had.'

'But that's a year ago,' said Jean.

'Quite true,' said Gopal Singh. 'But two months ago my
postal lorry was stopped on the road to Momeïk—the very
same road that you took to get here, and that you'll have to take
to get back to Rangoon. The rebels seized the money and
parcels, and only let the letters go through.

'And ten days ago, still, mind you, on that same road, two
policemen were kidnapped and nobody knows what became of
them.

'Then my drivers warned me that they didn't want to make
any more trips. But yesterday, fortunately, one of them had an
assurance that there would be no further risk attached to their
livelihood. One of his friends had gone over to the insurgents
and sent a message through.'

Suddenly Jean surprised everyone by giving a great roar of
laughter. He had just finished his second glass. He turned to me.

'I was just thinking of the heavy insurance you've taken out
against occupational risks. What fun it would be to arrange
with the insurgents to capture you!'

It was then that the man from Tibet spoke for the first time,
in a rather harsh but cultivated voice, carrying intelligence
with it.

'It's a pity I'm meeting you at so late a stage,' he said to
Jean, turning his lifeless eyes upon him and fixing him with
curious intentness. 'I might have tried to arrange something.'

'Do you know the insurgents?' I asked eagerly.

The Tibetan made a vague gesture.

'There are all kinds in this country,' he said. 'People who are
really fighting because of ideals . . . and the dacoits . . . and
further away, towards the frontier, the Chinese bands, and
nearer still the Shan nationalists.'

He bent his shaven head nearer the table in order to take
another noisy mouthful of tea.

'Once I was in the heart of the Shan region,' he went on, 'in an inn in the jungle run by a woman of the tribe. Some Burmese carriers stopped there. They drank the local wine'—he made a faint grimace of disgust—'a strong, bad alcohol that goes straight to the head. They insulted the woman at the inn. When they left, there was an ambush waiting for them. The Shans cut all their throats with the *dah*, the Burmese scimitar. They only spared one man, because he was an Indian.'

For a few moments the Tibetan fell into a reverie. His eyes looked so empty of meaning that he might have been blind.

'There are many interesting things round here,' he said. 'All the teak timber woods are under rebel control. Those are the idealists, and they're very well organized. As you know, the timber's right in the heart of the jungle, and no one has access to it except the woodcutters and the men who lead the troops of elephants who drag the wood to the river to be floated away. Well, the insurgents won't let the wood leave and they won't give the foresters a safe conduct until they've exacted from the company exploiting the forest a tax equal to that demanded by the government. Then they put their stamp on the cut wood. And since they've got observation posts all along the rivers, no timber can get through without their stamp.'

'It's quite true,' said Gopal Singh. 'I've seen the marks at Tabeytchin on the Irrawaddy and elsewhere.'

Julius took off his glasses and ran a nervous hand through his hair.

'They're very welcome to do any of that,' said he, 'as long as they leave Mogok alone.'

Suddenly he rounded fiercely on Jean.

'Did I hear you say "phantoms"?' he cried. 'That's nice and cool! What on earth do you think I live in that hovel on the main road for—for fun? I used to have a very nice house of my own choosing, right next to the police station. It was simply wonderful! The police station was attacked on two nights running. So I moved to an even better house on the outskirts of the town. It was absolutely splendid! I was on the route the partisans used to go back. My wall partitions were all punctured by bullets. There I was, under my bed all ready for the khazouk, when Gopal Singh, who knew I was alone, came rushing up with his gun.'

Julius mopped a few drops of sweat from his brow and carefully emphasized each word.

'That's what I call a brave man and a true friend!'

I turned towards our host.

'Did you manage to beat off the attack?' I asked.

Gopal Singh gave an ogre-like laugh which caused his beard to wag.

'Oh no,' he said. 'But as they were coming from several different sides, they fortunately shot one another. Incidentally, the police have already started dressing in civilian clothes.'

'Did you know,' went on Julius, 'that the important merchants bury their stock of sapphires and rubies in different places every night, because they're afraid of raids? And that they've only recently installed the telegraph system here—and entirely on account of the military situation? And that they have to keep the time the post leaves a secret, because of the rebels?'

Gopal Singh laughed again, flashing his white teeth and his burning eyes.

'It's perfectly true,' he said. 'The only trouble is that one of the post office employees is the brother of the head of the partisans.'

Jean's face suddenly took on a younger, more intense aspect. But this had nothing to do with the whisky he'd been drinking. It was due rather to happy memories of a time when he'd been outside the law himself, a leader in the secret resistance activities in occupied Savoy.

'It's just like the Maquis,' he whispered in my ear. 'It's wonderful, isn't it?'

Gopal Singh got up and paced up and down the room thoughtfully. Then he spoke gravely, his words echoing from his powerful chest.

'If I were you,' he said, 'I'd see that a rumour was spread in Mogok that you'd had to delay your departure for a week and then I'd leave eight days earlier, secretly, so as not to attract attackers on the journey.'

'Do you hear that?' cried Julius feverishly. He had to go with us as far as the airstrip at Momeïk.

But Kin Chone, his broker, spoke a few words to him in a low voice. And Julius sighed.

'Yes. I suppose it would be a safeguard to do that. There's only the point that the dealers will think there's another week for business. They'll hang on to their top price, and if we've got to leave without settling for the stones, our competitors will gain by the pretence.'

He sighed more deeply than ever.

'Whichever way you turn in this country you find you're in for the khazouk.'

'Well, what shall we do then?' asked Jean, visibly enjoying the dilemma that was agony to Julius.

But Julius, as always the *bon bourgeois* caught in the toils of adventure, decided in the end that business came first.

'Unfortunately,' said he, sadly, 'we've got to let the dealers know that there are only two days left for business.'

He looked at his watch and added:

'We must be off. The collective broker who represents the best dealers—you know that young man with the serious handsome face, who's already got nine children (nice and cool!)—will be at our office by now.'

As we rose to leave, the Tibetan spoke again.

'Forgive me if I'm delaying you,' he said. 'But this will only take a moment.'

He brought a little packet out of his waistcoat pocket and unwrapped it.

'I know from what Gopal Singh has said that you're experts. So I wondered if you'd mind . . .'

There was a ruby between his fingers.

'It's small, but a very fine one,' said Jean.

'It's a magnificent pigeon's blood stone,' added Julius, in confirmation.

The Tibetan seemed still to be waiting for something. The old Chinese broker bent over Julius's ear and began to whisper frantically.

Julius questioned him with the same excitement. Kin Chone was putting his case with the full weight of all his little bows, and all his grimaces.

'What's the matter?' asked Jean.

Julius answered as though against his will.

'He says he knew the original owner of the stone.'

'And who was that?' asked Julius.

The broker seemed scarcely to move his lips as he whispered the name:

'U Min Paw.'

With a sudden movement Jean turned back to the Tibetan.

'The famous bandit!' he cried. 'The famous treasure!'

The Tibetan said nothing, and it was Julius who spoke next.

'I don't know anything about it. I can remember only the biggest and most extraordinary of the stones.'

'But you've always told me that Kin Chone's visual memory was unique,' Jean reminded him.

It was Julius's turn to say nothing.

Jean turned to the man from Tibet.

'Where did you find the ruby?' he inquired.

'In Siam, when I went there on business,' he said. 'I think I bought it very cheaply.' Rapidly he gave the price in Siamese currency, which meant nothing to me.

But it did to Julius.

'Why, it was a gift,' he muttered.

'Whoever let you have it at such a low price?' asked Jean.

'A man in a hurry, no doubt.'

Julius began to hustle Jean towards the door.

'We're terribly late,' he complained.

His face wore that expression of alarm which never failed to appear upon it when anyone displayed curiosity about the treasure of U Min Paw.

On the stairs I managed to snatch a moment when Jean and I were standing near each other to speak to him.

'Listen,' I said quietly, 'you're not going to let me leave Mogok without telling me the whole story—I want to know how you've got on to the trail. You won't be risking anything now. We'll soon be miles away from here.'

I don't know whether it was the urgency of my tone, the whisky, or the bonds of friendship, but Jean weakened.

'I'll tell you on the way,' he said.

But on the way we had yet another encounter.

Gopal Singh, as hospitality demanded, had seen us on to the last step of the outside stairway which led from his house into the road. It was already nightfall, and the darkness had brought

with it, as always, the cool air from the mountains, like a bene-
diction after the infernal heat of the day. The moon was already
shining whitely upon the mountain peaks, the jungle, and, nearer
at hand, the roof-tops of Mogok.

Gopal Singh was making the customary long and flowery
speeches of farewell when, from the dark road behind the cross-
roads, a narrow track leading off towards the mountain, there
came a dull, heavy sound as of marching, accompanied by the
muted tinkling of little bells. A huge shape loomed up out of
the shadows, then another, and another, and another. Four
elephants came slowly forward, each with a driver perched upon
his nape.

The first moonbeams gleamed on their tusks and shed a
silvery sheen, like watered silk, over their grained and folded
hides.

This nocturnal procession had so fantastic a quality that for
a moment I felt all thought and feeling suspended. But as the
first elephant began to mount the road towards the great
mountain forests I exclaimed aloud:

'Where are they going?'

'They're going to the top of the mountain,' said Gopal Singh,
as though it were all the most ordinary thing in the world, 'to
fetch the forestry officer's furniture, because he's been posted
elsewhere. Then they'll bring him down, and all his large
family.'

When he saw my curiosity and interest, Gopal Singh turned
to me again.

'Would you like me to ask them to stop for a moment?' he
asked. 'I'm very friendly with the drivers. When they've spent
all their money on gambling or drink or anything else I sometimes let them have rice for nothing. And in return they help
me with their elephants for transporting goods.'

He hailed the man mounted on the foremost elephant and
shouted a few words to him in his own language. The driver,
who had bare feet, put the point of his big toe behind the great
floating, leaf-like ear of the elephant and gently scratched him.

Gopal Singh gave his ogre-like grin. 'Their skin is very
sensitive at that spot,' he said.

The elephant stopped. The driver made a brief, slow sound,
guttural, but also sing-song.

'Khmitt.'

The elephant didn't move.

'Khmitt,' sang the driver once again.

Then the huge beast gently, insensibly, sank down on his haunches, his back legs gradually folding under him. When his rump had touched the ground he lowered his forequarters. The driver slid along his flank and came up to us. The three others stayed perched on their elephants, their longis hanging like skirts. They made an extraordinary fresco outlined against the dark hills and the starry Burmese sky.

Jean and I were hypnotized by this spectacle. But Julius summoned his colleague back to reality.

'They're expecting us. . . . There are so many stones to see,' he said.

Jean sighed and set off on the way back to the town, walking between Julius and Kin Chone, who, being a Moslem, wore his sun-helmet even at night.

I stayed with Gopal Singh and the elephant driver, whom the moonlight revealed as a very small man, delicately made. His face was ageless: thin, cheerful and pleasant, netted with tiny wrinkles. He might have been forty, or sixty. But he was as lithe and lively as a lizard.

'*Oozie*,' said Gopal Singh, indicating him, 'from father to son.'

Thus I learned the Burmese name for an elephant driver.

The little man in the longi looked at me and laughed softly. Then he turned and spoke affably to Gopal Singh.

'He's amused at your curiosity,' said Gopal Singh. 'He says you're just like the other white men he's met, who are always fascinated by elephants. He says that he regards the elephant simply as a friend or a big brother.

'He rode an elephant for the first time—a small one, of course, when he was five. He's earned his living as an oozie ever since he was fifteen.'

I eagerly questioned Gopal Singh, and, through him, the little elephant driver. With the three vast animals standing by, the quiet little Burmese told me stories which took me to the very heart of the teak forests and jungles, where his own life was joined to those of the strongest and most intelligent animals in the world.

He told me that elephants lived about as long as men—to about eighty. Often, he said, when an oozie's future life was to be a settled one, if he happened to have been born at the same time as a baby elephant in the same jungle camp, they would learn their trade together, even fall in love for the first time at the same time, and continue thus all their lives, joined by an inexplicable bond bringing them closer and closer together until old age.

He explained how the young elephants were trained to endure the chains and saddles, to drag the trunks along, to carry men and other burdens, and to obey orders. It was not men who taught them best, he said, but the older and experienced elephants. They used their tusks as goads and their trunks as whips to teach the rudiments of the job to their little pupils.

Crouched at our feet in the roadside grass, he explained the motions that he went through in his work. Every driver, he said, washed down his elephant in the creeks or streams, using a piece of tree bark covered with soap. And every morning, he would go and find his own elephant in the jungle clearings, for the elephants were left at night to find their own food. An elephant could be recognized by the sound of two clappers on the outside of a hollow, bell-shaped piece of teak. No two of these bells ever sounded alike—at least, not to an oozie, who could always pick his own elephant out of a hundred others.

Because the elephants lived and fed under the same conditions as wild ones—among the forests and the bush—they were equally strong, and equally inured to the hazards and demands of their natural surroundings. They could cross rivers in full flood and break the backs of the fiercest tigers. Their lives were so near to those of elephants in their free state that this same oozie, whose monotonous sing-song voice was rising up to us out of the shadows, had spent a whole night sitting on his elephant's back amongst a herd of wild ones.

I asked him if he was one of the oozies who always kept to the same animal. He slowly shook his head, which was almost on a level with the ground.

No, he explained, this close relationship with one animal hadn't been possible for him, because of the war, which had left no time for settled ways.

Suddenly Gopal Singh began an animated discussion with

167

him. Then the Sikh's fierce but warm-hearted laughter rang out in the darkness.

'He retreated back to India, mounted on an elephant, with the British,' said Gopal Singh to me. 'And I was fighting the British, and must have been amongst those who were chasing him. And look at us now—the best friends in the world.'

The oozie had risen to his feet. I thought his face looked strangely sad, and I asked Gopal Singh the reason.

'The war and the Japanese,' the oozie explained, 'have brought enormous harm to the elephants. There used to be about seven thousand of them, and now there are only half.'

At that moment, another voice joined in. It was the harsh, deep voice of the Tibetan. Intrigued, perhaps, by Gopal Singh's long absence, he had come down the steps to join us, without my noticing him.

'I've often been in Siam,' he said, in English. 'And there's been the same destruction there. When the war ended there was such a demand for tame elephants that an American I knew made a fortune bringing in circus elephants that he'd bought for a very high price from European or American travelling shows. They'd probably been captured in Siam in the first place.'

I don't know if it was the advent of someone new upon the scene, boredom, or merely some reflex, but I saw a movement from the great crouched mass of the elephant who had led the procession. His bell gave a prolonged tinkle. To any ears, however inexpert, that must have sounded like a metallic noise.

I spoke to Gopal Singh, with a gesture towards the little Burmese.

'Does he say definitely that the bells are all of wood?' I asked.

There was no need for Gopal Singh to translate. The oozie had understood my surprise. Once more he gave his gentle smile.

'Metal bells are not usual,' he said, with Gopal Singh interpreting. 'They're only used to distinguish a dangerous elephant.'

His own was one. Only a short while before he had killed his driver, his driver's assistant, and another young elephant.

Whether this had been because of the rutting season, a sudden pain, or possession by some demon of the jungle, no one knew.

The animal had taken refuge in the jungle, but during the night it had prowled round the females. It could be recaptured then, provided it were approached properly with the right words of command.

The authorities regarded every trained elephant as precious, and they had sent for three men of the Karen tribe who were supposed to have an almost magical skill with elephants.

'Well,' said the oozie, with infinite scorn, 'being idiots, like all their tribe, the Karens spoke of what they were going to do in front of the females. Then, of course, the females warned the fugitive elephant.'

The oozie began to walk towards the elephant.

'As they were offering a big reward, I went to get him back. I knew an absolutely certain way of doing it.'

'And what was that?' I inquired.

It was the Tibetan who replied.

'He brought him some opium—in its raw state, of course.'

While I stood there incredulous, the Tibetan began to question the oozie in his own language.

'It's quite true,' said Gopal Singh. 'Since then his elephant and the others have been given two pounds of opium a day. It keeps them obedient and happy.'

His great laugh rang out.

'And you can be sure,' he added, 'that the drivers share it with them.'

'What, do the men and animals get drunk together?' I asked.

'Why not?' said the Tibetan.

'But where do they get the drug from?'

'The Shan country is the land of poppies,' said Gopal Singh. 'The government's generous with opium when it's for elephants.'

I was going to ask some more questions when the short, guttural, melodious cry rang out. The oozie had taken his place again on the elephant's neck.

'Tah! . . . Tah! . . .' he cried.

In the moonlight the animal reared up like a great Chinese

shadow, and the oozie again became a tiny figurine. His big toe touched the sensitive spot behind the big ear. The elephant mounted the path which led up the wooded mountain. One after the other, the other three followed him.

'Speaking of opium——' said the Tibetan.

That was all he said, but he took my arm and began to urge me towards Mogok.

The elephants had vanished in the dark forest. But one could still hear the dull beat of the three teak bells, and the sharp sound of the one metal bell.

We soon reached the first houses in Mogok, separated by only a few hundred yards from the spot where the elephants were now disappearing into the mountain forests.

The Tibetan was still silent, though it was he who was taking me on this walk.

The booths and stalls along the main road were all closed, and so were the workshops of the lapidaries. Only the living quarters on the first floors of all the identical houses were lit up.

In ours Jean, Julius and the broker were yet again absorbed in the task of examining sapphires and rubies. They had drawn the shutters in order to keep their business secret.

Facing them was the house of the Gujerati Indian, and there too the wall of teak was also shuttered up. But that was not enough to shut out the noise of the violent discussion that was going on inside. There were already some shadowy figures in longis standing still listening. My companion also stopped. There were loud cries, oaths and threats which could be clearly heard in the road. A few minutes passed and then the Tibetan spoke.

'I can see what's happened,' he said. 'The ruby merchant, who comes from Bombay, went back there some time ago. Before he left, the other Gujerati, whose voice you could hear raised so loudly a short while ago, gave him some money to give to his family. The dealer came back swearing that he'd done it, but the other one has now had a letter to say that it isn't true. That's why he isn't very pleased.'

He took me by the arm.

'Let's go on,' he said. 'It isn't very interesting. The man won't do anything except shout a few insults.'

We went on a little further.

'That's not like our Gopal Singh's father,' he went on. 'When he was in that position he stabbed the messenger who stole from him. The Sikhs are made of different stuff.'

As we went further along the main road it became quieter. But on the banks of the lake the silhouette of a tall, very thin figure in rags came to meet us, singing and reeling. Presently the old drunk drew level with me and suddenly recognized me. He sprang to attention, bringing his hand to his turban in a military salute. It was Julius's 'sweeper'. His magnificent, despairing eyes shone in the darkness. Following a habit that had grown between us, I gave him a few coins. He gave another salute and went uncertainly on his way.

'Drink!' said the Tibetan, quietly, but in such a tone of hatred and disgust that the word seemed for ever disgraced.

I remembered that when we were at Gopal Singh's house he had spoken of the effects of alcohol in this same tone.

'The sweeper often has a child with him,' he went on. 'Have you seen him?'

'He brings him to Julius's house,' I replied. 'He's a lovely little boy, with his grandfather's eyes.'

'He isn't his grandfather,' said the Tibetan. 'He's his father. Once, when he was dead drunk, he seduced his own daughter of twelve. When she had the child he was so ashamed that he sent her away, and gave a handful of rupees, which he'd begged, to a refuse collector, to marry her.'

There was something extraordinary about the wealth and precision of detail.

'You seem to know Mogok very well,' I said.

'The seamy side particularly,' he replied.

'But you don't come from the town?'

'I travel about a good deal, and often stop here,' he said.

'How is it Julius hadn't seen you before?' I asked. 'He knows everyone in Mogok.'

'As I told you, I'm mainly interested in the lower stratum of Mogok.'

'But how did we come to meet you this evening, then?'

'You will understand,' said the Tibetan quietly, 'after friend-ship over the tray.'

He would not explain himself.

At that moment we had rounded the end of the lake and arrived in what was by far the poorest quarter of Mogok. With its uneven alleyways, cut by areas of open or waste land, it looked like a land of outcasts or lepers. We passed a ruined pagoda, and, a little lower down, a Buddhist monastery. The Tibetan paused a moment in front of it, and inclined his shaven head. Then, with an almost brutal gesture of decision, he went towards a neighbouring house, a wretched, crooked, dilapidated building from which issued neither light nor sound.

The Tibetan knocked on the rickety door. His blows were discreet to begin with, but they became louder and louder until, with a terrible creaking sound, the whole arrangement of rotting planks opened a little way. It was no more than a chink. But, though narrow, it was enough to allow the escape of an atmosphere of such foulness that it seemed to taint the purity of the night air.

A cadaverous face showed itself in the opening. It had the sort of dead, dry, grey skin that one might find on a skull, and the eyes were nothing more than two black holes. The man briskly shook his death's head to show that we couldn't go in. But the Tibetan had only to whisper a few words for the expression on the spectral face to change at once into a deferential, obsequious smile. The door opened a little wider, just enough to let us glide inside; then it shut suddenly like a trap. The smell, which seemed to go right to the marrow of my being, was laden at one and the same time with the worst odours which untended human bodies can give off, and the deep, smooth, rich smell of opium. We were in a dung-heap of the most sordid kind.

There was only one room. It had musty partitions and a floor covered with rubbish. There was no furniture there, but, all along the walls, there ran rudimentary benches, made of disjointed planks covered with filthy refuse. On each of them there were two, three, or four men stretched out or entwined, next to an opium lamp. The dull light from their wicks was the only illumination in the room, where the smoke grew thicker and thicker all the while.

My companion stood on the threshold for a moment contemplating the sight. None of the smokers seemed to notice our presence. Some were filling or smoking their pipes, others, their eyes closed, were dreaming, while others talked quietly to one another.

'The second wisdom in the world,' said the Tibetan.

'And the first?' I asked.

'That facing us.'

I understood him to mean the Buddhist monastery before which he had inclined his head.

The skull-faced proprietor glided between the benches and came to find us. He made a suggestion to my companion, but the latter refused.

'He offered us his room,' said the Tibetan. 'But I like the company of poor men. They can teach one much.'

With this double-edged remark he allowed himself to be led to the only empty couch in the room. It belonged to the owner himself, and was covered with a clean mat. When we were stretched on either side of the tray I spoke to my companion.

'Are there many places like this in Mogok?'

'There are about ten.'

'Isn't it forbidden in Burma?'

'Yes,' he replied. 'And so it is in India and Siam and Viet-Nam and Hong Kong. But people smoke everywhere. And everywhere the ban on smoking brings in large sums to the police. I can see one here, incidentally.'

With the shaft of his pipe, of which he was just warming the bowl, he indicated a man stretched out like the others, and in no way distinguishable from them. He was smoking opium in long, regular draughts.

The death's head appeared in the aura of our lamp. He put down on the tray a little jar containing a fresh supply of the black drug.

My companion began to roll a pellet.

'Where does the opium come from?' I asked.

'This region is surrounded by poppy fields. There's Shan, Siam, and China. And there's such extensive smuggling that not a single one of the things found in the shops—watches, fountain-pens, chemist's goods, photographic equipment— comes into Mogok by the legal channel. So you can imagine how it is with opium!'

The Tibetan was now cooking his pellet of opium on the point of a needle in the lamp flame.

'Recently a ton of opium was delivered here all at once,' he said.

I raised myself on one elbow.

'What!' I cried. 'A ton!'

'Oh, it doesn't take many of those little horses from Tibet that you've seen about in the country. When they've got pack-saddles on both sides they can bring in a considerable amount.'

While I was picturing in my mind's eye the procession of long-maned ponies and little yellow men, crossing frontiers, jungle and mountains, the landlord returned. This time he brought us some pale boiling tea. He had not made any for his other clients.

'Why is he looking after us like this?' I asked the Tibetan, who was just finishing his first pipe.

'Because it's I who brought in the caravan with the ton of opium.'

He added, in the same indifferent tone of voice:

'You smoke yourself, I hope?'

'Like you, I'm widely travelled,' I replied. He offered me the bamboo pipe.

'The only thing is, that I don't know how to prepare a pipe.'

'I'll do it for you,' said the Tibetan. 'I know only too well.'

The opium was good. Under its influence, the air became easier to breathe and the place pleasanter. I used it with moderation, however. I wanted to keep my head clear. My companion, on the other hand, was smoking copiously, and as the pellets melted and spluttered in the bowl of his pipe his eyes and other features became infused with a little more life and human warmth. I didn't need to question him: as he smoked he talked of his own mental agony, like a man unleashed from himself.

When he was very young he had believed that his vocation was to be a bonze: a priest dedicated to an ascetic life as a beggar. He thought that he had the necessary devoutness and steadfastness of will.

He had been happy during his time as a student in an ancient monastery on the slopes of the Roof of the World, where the standard of learning was high and the rule strict. But it was then that a traveller had made him taste poppy juice for the first time. And that was his revelation. A light thrown upon himself. A truth from which there was no way back.

'From that time I knew that I was unworthy to attain the first wisdom, which is complete renunciation,' said the Tibetan. 'So I returned to the life of men.'

But, despite every effort, his original vocation held him for ever on the outskirts of ordinary life. Because his conscience made him feel outside the law, by a curious inner response he had become literally outside the law. He made his living by all forms of illegal traffic. With the Far East in its present state of upheaval he found an unlimited field there.

I asked him if he had grown rich as a result.

'I haven't a rupee,' he said. 'Everything I earn by trafficking in arms, drugs, and so forth, goes to the monastery.'

He gazed thoughtfully at the lamp and added with deep humility:

'It is for each to redeem himself as best he can.'

He put down his pipe, lay down on his back and remained immobile for a long time, with his eyes closed.

The other benches looked like strange rafts floating in the smoke, each with a cargo of peaceful emaciated faces.

Without moving or opening his mouth, my companion began to talk as though he were dreaming aloud.

'Men—men——' he said. 'I can hear a Chinese on my right. He comes from the border region held by bands who claim to be adherents of Chiang Kai-shek. It's rich opium country. He's asking the miner facing him how he can exchange opium for precious stones.'

A smile both ironic and ecstatic—a Buddhist smile—played upon his lips. Then his voice rose once more:

'Further on, there's a policeman sharing his tray with a Communist rebel. The insurgent has been wounded in an encounter with government troops and he's managed to slip into Mogok to be looked after by a doctor friend of his. The policeman's giving him directions to houses where he can find arms. Now—just a moment—the rebel's talking to the policeman about a very rich mine. It's inside the mountain where his group of partisans are sheltering. No one other than themselves can gain access to it. The insurgents dig for rubies and the doctor friend disposes of them. But now they've had some bad luck. The doctor trusted an important lot to a pilot who had to get them into India and sell them. But when he came back he swore that the Customs had taken the stones. How can one tell if this is true?'

Slowly the Tibetan raised his lids. His hand did not grope as he took his pipe. I questioned him about the dacoits.

'The dacoits are as old as Upper Burma itself,' was all the reply he gave at first.

Then he smoked again, and resumed.

'When you come from Tabeytchin, the Irrawaddy port, there's a mule path that crosses the village of Khin, which was famous even under the kings of Mandalay for the toughness of its brigands. At the side of the road there's a stone with an inscription in English engraved on it.'

With no apparent effort he recited the inscription:

'In memory of Jemadar Adjutant Dewi Sahaï Nisr and Sepoy Javala Singh, of the police battalion belonging to the Ruby Mine Company, who died in action against the dacoits on this spot on December 18th, 1889.'

'What a memory!' I said.

The former bonze gave a melancholy smile.

'In our monasteries,' he replied, 'one exercises the memory first of all.'

From the way he had begun to smoke again I felt that it would be a long series of pipes. I got up from the seat. The Tibetan did nothing to keep me. All he said was this:

'Would you please tell your friend Jean that I will call to discuss certain stones with him. They're from the same source as the ruby I asked his opinion about when we were with Gopal Singh, but very much more important.'

Swiftly I bent over the face lit by the opium lamp.

'What? The vanished treasure—the former dacoit who became the most important collector of precious stones?'

But the Tibetan, his eyes closed, went on smoking.

*   *   *

I returned to Jean as quickly as I could. He was already in his camp-bed but I hauled him off to my room and gave him the message. Then I said:

176

'And now that I've unintentionally become a link in the chain, you must explain it all to me.'

'Well,' said he, 'suppose that an Indian with whom my family had had business dealings for a long time came to Paris, and that he'd stopped at Colombo, and that there he'd met a Siamese doctor who'd told him that at Bangkok some very beautiful stones were being sold secretly and that people were saying that they came from a fantastic collection from Mogok. And suppose that on the way I encountered the Siamese and that he suggested that I should wait at Mogok for a contact from him?'

Jean, who rarely smoked, lit a cigarette. He paused for a few moments before he spoke again.

'Suppose——' he said. 'And then forget.'

'What are you afraid of?' I asked. 'We're leaving the day after tomorrow.'

'Well, that depends on what the Tibetan has to tell me,' Jean replied.

16

On our last day in Mogok, I saw the grandmother of the valley of rubies.

This was Daw Pouanyine, who was ninety-five years old.

Half a century before, she had taught the science of precious stones to Daw Hla, who had once kept her family by peddling rice from mine to mine, but now owned the finest reserve of sapphires and rubies in the valley. Maung Khin Maung came to find us one morning in order to take us to see the old lady. I was the only one who went with him, Jean giving the first plausible excuse that came to mind for staying with Julius. Actually, he was afraid to go out in case he missed the Tibetan.

Daw Pouanyine lived on the other bank of the lake, but on the opposite side from the opium den that I had visited the previous night. It was a modest part of the town, to which the trees and the rather wild gardens gave a certain countrified charm. The brown colour of the walls, which were sagging slightly, indicated that the house where the old lady lived was very old. In other respects, it differed in no way from all the other houses, both rich and poor, where I had so often been welcomed. There was the same outside stairway, serving as the only entrance into the usual large room where the families led their day-to-day lives and received visitors.

At Daw Pouanyine's house, however, the room was entirely bare and the old lady herself was sitting on the mat with her legs crossed under her, wrapped in a longi of grey and blue check.

The first emotion which she inspired was a strong feeling of tenderness and affection. When one saw her, one thought, not that she had reached the limits of life, but rather that the wear and tear of time had taken from her all material weight and coarser substance. Sitting upon the straw mat, she was so slender and fragile, so devoid of flesh, with her tiny head beneath its white hair held very erect between her insubstantial shoulders, that she looked remarkably like a shrivelled little bird.

In front of her knees, within reach of her hand, there was a cup of tea, a bowl of rice, and a copper tray covered with precious stones.

Spread around her were her grandchildren, her grandchildren's children, and her grandchildren's children's children. There was even a new-born baby of the fifth generation.

When the grandmother replied to my questions through Maung Khin Maung, her voice, naturally a little cracked, was none the less as bright and lively as the look in her piercing little black eyes.

Yes indeed, the old lady said. She had come to Mogok from Taungyi, the capital of the Shan States, when she was a very young girl. The almost thousand-mile journey had been by buffalo cart. How else could she have come? It was the only way in those days.

Burma was under the despotic rule of King Thibaw, the last sovereign to bear the title of the Golden Feet. He ruled from amid the splendours of his palace in Mandalay. To him alone the ruby mines belonged, and to him alone all valuable stones had to be rendered.

Yes, said Daw Pouanyine, any coolies caught defrauding the Crown of its rights were tortured. But the king himself was not a wicked man. The whole blame lay with the avarice and savagery of his officers.

For Daw Pouanyine herself had been to Mandalay, the city of cities, travelling on mule back to Tabetychin on the Irrawaddy, and then down the river in a sailing junk. And in Mandalay, with her own mortal eyes, Daw Pouanyine had beheld the last of the Burmese kings, clad in gold, coming out of the great gold-crowned pagoda. And behind him came the dignitaries under their triple-tiered golden sunshades, and in front of him strode the sacred elephant who wore as an ear-ring in his right ear the matchless ruby found by Nga Mauk—the Royal Ruby that was as large as a hen's egg.

Yes, these were the things Daw Pouanyine had seen.

And then she had seen the white men come with their terrible cannon and their Indian soldiers who never spared women. But she had been craftier than they, and she had found a good hiding-place.

The frail silhouette on the mat was shaken gently by a little cracked crystalline laugh.

'Do you know where she hid from the British in 1884?' asked Maung Khin Maung. 'In those same mines, in the depth of the Hollow Mountain, where I hid from the Japanese in 1944.'

I heard the grandmother's voice again, and this time she seemed to be talking with more spontaneity. Her life, she said, had been long, and it had been good. It was true of course that she hadn't been as lucky as Paya Taga U Hlat, who started work in the mines as poor as she was herself, but who, having the gift of finding beautiful stones by the handful, had made such a huge fortune that he had been known as the Ruby King. But he'd been dead a long time now, whereas she, Daw Pouanyine, was still here, able to see the flowering of a fifth generation of descendants. To crown her happiness there was only one thing she wished for. That was to await the close of her days in Taungyi, the town she had left almost a century ago. And she would like to travel the thousand miles from Mogok to Taungyi by the same means that she had come—in a buffalo cart.

She turned towards her grandsons and their sons' sons.

'I've taught you all,' she said. 'Remember never to let a pregnant woman go near the bayon, because if you do it will be poor in rubies. And never bring into a mine mushrooms, fish, hen's eggs, venison or the meat of the wild boar. To find fertile spots consult the Pundjis saints (the bonzes) about their dreams, watch the signs of the moon that I have shown you, and above all try to find where the end of the rainbow lies.'

The old lady suddenly stopped speaking and sat there with her head erect, all creased and wrinkled, a strange, weightless, fleshless little bird whose eyes seemed to be gazing along the invisible course of her own life's rainbow, to a point beyond its end.

* * *

I went home about midday, only to learn from Jean that the man from Mogok hadn't put in an appearance.

Nor had there been any sign of him when the time came for our last dinner in Mogok.

* * *

We had been invited to a farewell dinner at Daw Hla's house. Although it was contrary to custom for a woman to be present at a formal banquet, Daw Hla nevertheless sat at the head of her own table. No doubt her position as a widow and the mistress of her family, her business, and the most important stock of precious stones in Mogok exempted her from this rule. Besides, she never spoke a word nor ate a mouthful, content to remain a wise and gentle guardian, looking on and smiling at the guests her son had chosen.

Maung Khin Maung had invited all his friends. Julius was there, of course, with his old Chinese broker, and Ko Ba Ve, late of the rue Lafayette, who spoke French and even *argot*, and so were the old tic-tormented pirate and his nonchalant nephew. Finally, there was one face we had not seen before: a young man of about thirty with a cheerful expression who burst out laughing on the slightest provocation.

'He's been a very close friend since childhood,' said Maung Khin Maung, of this young man. 'Last week he found a rough ruby in the mine in which he has a partnership, and it was so beautiful that I bought it at once for thirty-five thousand rupees.

'He immediately invited all his friends and acquaintances to a big banquet. He drank and gambled with them, and now he's got nothing left, while I've got the ruby. I feel rather guilty. As a sort of atonement I asked him to come to this dinner in your honour.'

'But he never stops laughing,' I said.

Maung Khin Maung thoughtfully bowed his delicate head.

'He thinks that from now on his fingers have been specially favoured and will bring him good luck.'

As he spoke the word a sudden deep silence settled upon the whole table. Then suddenly eyes became brighter, voices louder and more vibrant. The room seemed charged with strange currents.

'Look at them,' whispered Julius. 'They're in their element: gambling fever. They're so fond of gambling that they actually have sweepstakes on the day and time of arrival of the monsoon —nice and cool, eh?'

As he spoke, Julius took off his glasses more nervously than ever.

'All the same,' he went on, rather feverishly, 'one can't deny the fact that some people are always getting the khazouk and others are always having strokes of luck. Think of that poor woman who was picking over stones from the waste products of a mine. She had to relieve herself and moved away. When she squatted down her absent gaze happened to alight on a magnificent sapphire!'

Already the air around us was humming with stories no less remarkable.

'And look at me,' said Ko Ba Ve. 'I let a mine go dirt cheap because after a whole year of being worked it was completely sterile, and what happens but that the very day after the sale they find a huge ruby there!'

Meanwhile Julius was tugging at my sleeve.

'Ramsay—that American——' he was saying. 'He came here before the war with so little money that he couldn't buy any proper stones. He kept himself down to lots of hardly any value at all. Amongst one of them, right at the bottom of the scale, there were some rubies with stars in the centre. At the time that was regarded as such a flaw that any sale of the stone could be rendered null and void. He bought handfuls of them for practically nothing and took them back to America. The women there became mad on star rubies and now they're the most expensive stones you can find. Ramsay made his fortune almost overnight.'

The shrill voice of Kin Chone, the old broker, rose above the others.

'Do you remember those two brothers,' he cried, 'Ky Oa Sin, and his younger brother Nga Moh? They each bought a new mine, but Nga Moh found a rock in his way which stopped him from going any further. So he asked Ky Oa Sin, whose bayon was fertile, if he could have an equal share and work in his mine. The older brother agreed, and they worked the same bayon together. When they deposited the soil dug from the mine they each took one side of the channel through which the monsoon water would flow when the time came. The monsoon came and the stream flooded and washed the pile of soil. Ky Oa Sin's contained magnificent rough stones—and there was nothing at all on Nga Moh's side.'

Kin Chone had scarcely finished speaking before the old

pirate's nephew struck up. What had become of his customary nonchalance, I wondered. His eyes were bright and his face tense.

'Ky Oa Sin and Nga Moh—why, that's nothing!' he cried. 'What about the other two brothers, U Po Shwe and Maung Toke San? They also took mines at the same time. And U Po Shwe, the elder one, prospered, while Maung Toke San was ruined. So Maung Toke San asked his elder brother to let him have part of his mine. U Po Shwe, being generous and fond of his brother, didn't just let him have a share—he gave up the whole thing to him, and then went to find another one elsewhere. And what do you think happened then? Maung Toke San couldn't find any more stones in the bayon his brother had left him, while right next to him, U Po Shwe made his fortune again!'

At this tale everyone round the table, amongst them those who already knew the story well, exchanged solemn and awed glances. Maung Khin Maung, as though to excuse their strong feelings, spoke to me quietly:

'There's nothing you can do about it. Life is just a gamble. There's luck in everything; in the bayon, in the rough mineral. A share in a mine is nothing but a lottery ticket. When a coolie plunges his hands in the ruby earth, it's as though he had thrown the dice.'

He was thoughtful for a moment. When he began to speak again his voice was still soft, but firm and confident.

'All the same,' he went on, 'there is a way of directing the course of one's luck. That's by following the old traditional teachings. One must never commit a sin while working in the mine. Above all, one must never undercut. And if one throws down rice or any other food in a mine one can be sure that the bayon will yield nothing. The proof of that is that an envious person has only to throw a few grains of rice into the entrance to your mine to render it completely infertile. And, of course, it's absolutely essential when one starts work on a mine-bed to have all the coolies dressed in white cloth.'

Then Maung Khin Maung told me about the offerings he had to make to the *Nats*, minor, but very influential deities.

Jean, who was listening to this conversation, smiled.

'I believe you're superstitious,' he said.

'What me, superstitious!' cried Maung Khin Maung, with the greatest sincerity. 'Not in the least, I assure you.'

'Then why do you refuse to engage in any conversation about the famous sapphire?' asked Jean.

The youthful chiselled features of Maung Khin Maung were lit up by an indulgent smile.

'In honour of your departure,' he said, lowering his voice, 'I'll confide in you the secret of the sapphire. It all happened on our New Year's Day. You know that that's an occasion when we entertain ourselves rather like children, especially by splashing one another with water when we're fully dressed. Well, while I was engaged in this game a coolie from the mine I was working came running up out of breath to warn me that they'd made a beautiful find. Without changing my clothes, which were streaming with water, I rushed to the mine. The find was this sapphire. How can I sell, even to you, a blessing which came to me on New Year's Day?'

Maung Khin Maung's eyes, as he fixed them upon Jean, shone with the strength of his conviction.

'That's not superstition at all,' he said. 'It's having respect for luck.'

Jean smiled amiably and glanced at his watch.

'Now,' he said, 'I shall have to go and see if luck's waiting for me at Julius's house.'

But U Nyo, our old Burmese servant, whom Julius had left in charge, hadn't seen even the shadow of the Tibetan during our absence.

* * *

It was our last morning in Mogok.

When I opened the teak shutters the witch-like clouds were still floating on the lake as though to enchant and hold us there for ever. But I knew that in a few hours Daw Hla's beautiful American car would come and take us to the landing-ground at Momeïk.

Jean and I had decided to make a second farewell visit to Daw Hla. This was not from excessive politeness, but because we felt a sort of inner reluctance—a curious sense of grief—at leaving her.

As it was still early, we surprised her while she was still busy with household affairs. She was measuring and folding huge pieces of material in the characteristic shades of ochre, saffron and orange which were worn by the Buddhist monks and priests. Her son was helping her.

'Do you also sell robes to the bonzes then?' I asked Maung Khin Maung, in joke.

But his face as he replied remained very serious.

'These pieces of stuff are a gift from my mother to a hundred young men of humble family for a great initiation ceremony. It's to be held very shortly, on the day when my mother's grand-son—my married sister's child—begins his studies and is to be received in the great monastery.'

Jean indicated the material.

'You'd think there was enough for millions,' he said quietly.

'On the same day,' went on Maung Khin Maung, 'there's to be a ceremony of dedication, with an accompaniment of gongs and flutes, of a pagoda my mother has had built, in order to gain merit.'

I looked at the round peaceful face of Daw Hla, illuminated at that moment as with a light from within.

'You've still got enough time to come and see the pagoda,' said Maung Khin Maung. He smiled faintly and added: 'After all, you're the great expert on Buddhism.'

I turned to Julius who had deliberately spread the legend. He had apparently decided to play it out to the end.

'Yes,' he said, not without severity. 'It's quite true.'

Jean, as on the day before, declined to come with us, because he still hoped to see the Tibetan.

Soon I was standing alone with Maung Khin Maung on a hill which offered a view of great splendour and serenity. Before us stood a temple as white as innocence, divided inside by galleries of pillars and crowned with a needle which the work-men were beginning to cover with gold leaf. Maung Khin Maung showed me the place of worship where the statue of Buddha was soon to be enthroned, the chamber reserved for the bonze who was to be spiritual director of the place, and the cell for the pupil who would wait on him.

After that Maung Khin Maung took me to another hill. There a vast group of buildings towered up, enclosed by low walls and with the spires of the sanctuary rising up above them.

'This is the monastery,' he said, 'where my sister's young son is coming to be instructed—as all the men in the family have been—at the source of the smiling wisdom and meditation.'

I followed Maung Khin Maung through the enclosure, which had no one guarding it. A path which meandered through the shadows and flowers of the great garden led us to the central part of the monastery. This was a vast hall ventilated by galleries supported by pillars. Valuable wood, polished and darkened by time, covered the walls. About a hundred little children were seated on the stone floor studying sacred texts. At the back there were some steps leading up to the altar. There, in front of huge statues of Buddha, the shaven-headed bonzes were collecting into their wooden bowls the rice which their disciples had begged for them. The young men were waiting on them during their frugal meal, and then assisting them at their ablutions.

'This monastery has plenty of very pure water,' said Maung Khin Maung.

A few minutes later he showed me in the cloistered enclosure a vast, deep cistern, bearing an inscription in Burmese on the side.

'It's the name of my elder brother,' said Maung Khin Maung. 'As you know, he died in Paris. My mother had this cistern dug for the monks and priests in memory of him.'

When I praised Daw Hla's generosity he replied modestly:

'Everyone here is glad to gain a little merit. We believe that it makes our life hereafter easier and lends dignity to it. There isn't a ruby dealer here, even amongst the least fortunate, who hasn't built at least one pagoda. Some very devout men build one for every beautiful stone they find.'

We had left the cloister now. Round us the mountains and hills stretched into infinity. And all the summits were sown and scattered with temples. Sometimes their walls gleamed white and new, sometimes time had turned them to bronze and ash-grey. I wondered how many sapphires and rubies they had had to find to make that valley bristle as it did with golden needles.

On the way back, Maung Khin Maung showed me yet another pagoda. It was the biggest and most highly ornamented in

Mogok, he said, containing three Buddhas all sparkling with gold and jewels.

In the galleries, women of all ages were laughing and chatting and smoking little cheroots. Before the holy statues there were two young girls on their knees, with their foreheads touching the ground. Smiling, Maung Khin Maung called one of them by name. She raised her head and smiled back at him. They exchanged a few pleasant words and then the two young girls returned to the exercise of their religion, the least demanding and most indulgent in the world.

At the back of the pagoda was something which looked exactly like one of the slot machines to be found in European and American bars and saloons. I drew Maung Khin Maung's attention to it and he began to laugh silently, as he put a little copper coin into the slot. This set the springs in motion and a procession of marionettes began. A young Eastern nobleman was going off with his companions, while a weeping woman leaned out of a window.

'It's the departure of Buddha for his great solitude,' Maung Khin Maung told me.

Another movement of the springs put an end to this picturesque and mystical little sideshow.

A frieze composed of paintings, each one representing a pagoda, ran the whole length of the wall opposite. I counted sixteen of them. They had all been built by the same man, who had also built the one where we now stood. He had spent hundreds of millions of rupees.

I inquired from my companion about this devout and generous character.

'He died recently,' said Maung Khin Maung. 'But you can see his face.'

He took me to a corner of the gallery. There I had a violent shock. Inside a glass cabin an old man was sitting on a chair gazing at me fixedly through his spectacles. It took me a second to realize that he was made of wax. It was all the accessories—his longi, jacket, sandals and glasses—which gave him so disturbingly lifelike an appearance. I studied his face. Its expression was ascetic, studious, and very hard.

A copper plaque gave his name but I couldn't read Burmese writing. However, these characters did seem vaguely familiar.

I racked my memory and suddenly it came to me. They were the same letters as those on the ring I had found in front of the impenetrable mines of the Hollow Mountain, which had sheltered Maung Khin Maung, when he had fled from the Japanese; Daw Pouanyine, when, sixty years before, she had fled from the British; and, at every period, all the exiles, bandits and dacoits.

I had often gazed at the seal on my ring and thought about the man who had owned it. I drew it out of my pocket once more and compared the letters. They were identical.

The name formed on my lips:

'U Min Paw.'

A shudder passed down my spine. This waxwork mask gazing at me with a pitiless eye was a replica of the former murderer's face—the man who had owned the stones which Jean was seeking, and which the Tibetan had said——

With all speed I was driven back to Julius's house.

The Tibetan hadn't come.

17

I CLOSED the door of my room and spoke to Jean in a low voice.

'What shall we do now?'

Jean's face was tense and his eyes did not move. I understood only too well the inner debate in which he was engaged.

Daw Hla's car, which was to take us over the thirty-seven miles of bad road to the landing-ground at Momeïk, had already been waiting for a long time in front of the house. We had waited now until the limit. A few more minutes and we ran the risk of missing the plane, our only link with the outside world until another week had elapsed.

And yet—how could we leave Mogok at the moment when the secret of the vanished rubies seemed about to be revealed —when the trail to U Min Paw's royal treasure was just beginning?

Jean answered my question with one of his own.

'Are you quite positive that the Tibetan was serious? He wasn't drunk with opium?'

I would have been glad to have delivered Jean from his dilemma by unloading, as it were, one side of the balance. But I had seen the former bonze using opium as the food of a perfectly lucid and almost brotherly understanding. The drug in no way touched his intellect, his energy, or his memory. The fact that he had left the opium den leaving no trace, and that Gopal Singh knew nothing of his last movements, could mean only that this was how he had wanted it to be. It would be a decision made firmly and clearly, and of his own free will.

When I expressed these views to Jean I heard him utter a muffled oath.

'It's quite clear,' he said at last. 'He only showed us the small ruby to indicate that he held the key to the finer ones. But why hasn't he shown up here, after his promise? Yes—I know—he's been prevented. But we've no means of knowing if he'll come back within a week, or a month, or ever.'

He swore again. He had a temperament which couldn't bear a state of indecision. And here he was, driven right into a corner.

Julius, without knowing that he did so, came to the rescue. He came in briskly, taking off his glasses.

'It's hardly worth our getting killed by the dacoits if you're going to miss the plane anyway,' he exclaimed.

Julius was coming with us. All our arguments and pleading had failed to dissuade him from seeing us to Momeïk. This journey, which he would have to make twice in the same day, made him feel ill in advance. But the demands of hospitality, courtesy and affection were once more thrusting Julius, honest bourgeois that he was, on to the path of adventure.

'Yes,' he went on, 'I'm always pleased to run the risk of dacoits, but I do like it to be for some purpose.'

Jean gazed for a moment at his old friend's face, harassed alike by fear and an impatient desire to get the ordeal over. He answered him very gently:

'We're coming, Julius. We're coming. Now are you satisfied?'

'Nice and cool,' muttered Julius.

His favourite phrase had never sounded so lugubrious and yet so comic. But this time I didn't feel like laughing. Now that our departure was simply a matter of seconds, I had a bitter sense of disappointment. Jean's passionate enthusiasm for the treasure of U Min Paw had infected me more than I realized. To have to leave Mogok without solving the riddle, and just at the moment when the answers seemed to be at hand, filled me with unendurable frustration.

But what could we do? The old Chinese broker was already settled in the car.

He was probably even more scared than Julius. But just as Julius couldn't abandon us, so Kin Chone couldn't abandon Julius.

So once more we set out on the road between Mogok and Momeïk. But this time our feelings were reversed. The pangs of homesickness at parting with an enchanted world which we were to lose for ever replaced those former delicious sensations of anticipation and discovery, as we had neared the splendid, secret threshold.

'Ah well——' said Jean, when the last houses of Mogok had vanished between the screen of jungle.

At the first defile which could have lent itself to an ambush, Julius removed his glasses. This nervous gesture was one which we were now well able to interpret.

'Go on with you,' cried Jean. 'We're still near the town.'

'Where the khazouk's concerned,' grumbled Julius, 'there's no such thing as far or near.'

As though to prove his point, three armed men stepped out of the bush and, pointing their guns at the car, ordered the chauffeur to stop.

But they were only policemen.

They made a thorough investigation of each one of us, without replying to the questions Julius and his broker asked. Then they let us go.

'That's weird,' muttered Julius. 'I've never known them so zealous!'

'Well, that's fine,' said Jean. 'The road's guarded.'

'Yes, but why?' asked Julius, anxiously.

It was then that Jean, either to distract him from his nervousness, or because he felt it necessary to put him in the picture, began to explain the matters which he had been keeping from him.

'You remember how, in Paris, I had some news about U Min Paw's treasure,' he said, 'and that the other evening I thought I'd reached the end of the trail—when we were at——'

Julius interrupted him. His shoulders and eyebrows rose.

'You're not telling me anything I don't know already,' he growled, '—when we were at Gopal Singh's, and met that charlatan of a Tibetan.'

Julius's massive, harassed face was shaken up and down as the car jolted over the jungle track. Jean gazed at his colleague.

'So you guessed then?' he said.

'I could have done that without having had four years in counter-espionage.'

'And didn't you want to come and help me, even for a moment?'

'I know nothing about that business,' Julius replied. 'And I don't want to know anything.'

'But all the same,' said Jean, 'what if the Tibetan were to approach you after I've gone?'

'No,' said Julius. 'No.'

His face wore such a combination of obstinacy and fear that Jean began to laugh.

'Oh dear,' he said. 'You're getting as superstitious as the Burmese.'

'Superstitious or not,' said Julius firmly, 'that whole story stinks to high heaven of the khazouk, and I don't want to talk about it any more.'

On the first of the little wooden bridges which spanned a ravine, three policemen were lying in the wild undergrowth. They came out and stopped the car—for another silent investigation.

'Something must have happened,' said Julius, feverishly, 'when we set out—or else something's going to happen.'

But we reached the landing-ground at Momeïk without incident.

The aeroplane for Mandalay and Rangoon was already waiting in the centre of the rectangle which had been roughly hewn in the bush.

As on the day we arrived, Burmese soldiers in huge felt hats, their fingers poised on their triggers, were placed all round the field to protect cargoes and travellers from rebels and dacoits. The same motley crowd as before jostled round the plane. But this time there was only one white man amongst them. This was the American missionary whom we had seen at the same spot when we landed.

Julius, from mere politeness, went up to him, intending only to exchange a few commonplace and, above all, brief remarks.

But suddenly he began to shout at us with all his might and beckon us towards him.

'Listen!' he shouted. 'Come and listen to the padre!'

The man in the flowered shirt was grinding the end of his cigar between his teeth as though he would turn it to powder, and he looked much more like something out of Hollywood than a man of the church. He had a round, full, fresh face, a strong and greedy-looking jaw, alert and cheerful eyes, and large hands less suited to the act of blessing than to playing baseball. There was soothing unction only in his voice, and this arose from the fact that he spoke English in the soft, drawling, sing-song manner of an American from the Southern States.

When he saw that he had two new white members of his audience, both strangers to the country, he started his story again with unconcealed pleasure. There was nothing in his expression, his manner, or his tone of voice to prepare us for the strangeness and cruelty of the tale we were to hear.

'Well,' said he, 'it all happened to me the day before yesterday.' He rolled his cigar between his lips. 'In the morning— when I was driving along in my old truck that you see over there.'

He gestured with his cigar towards the dusty and battered old jeep at the side of the landing-ground.

'Julius'll tell you that I spend the best part of my time going round from one village to another. I've got good pals all over the place. How many conversions I make is another thing altogether. You can't sell Christianity very easily in a country like this. The people accept the Bible in Burmese charmingly, put it carefully on one side and then ask me to a mahjong party. They say they acquire merit by playing with a servant of the Lord. What would you do in my place? Besides, to tell you the truth, if you can't get a game of poker, mahjong's not so bad.'

Julius interrupted with manifest impatience.

'Please do come to the point, padre!' he cried. 'The coolies are finishing loading the plane.'

'Sure,' said the missionary. 'In this country you only meet Europeans for a few moments, never for long enough to play poker.'

He sighed so deeply that a large piece of ash fell off his cigar on to his flowered shirt.

'Well, yesterday morning,' he went on, 'I was about a hundred miles from here, north of the Mogok country. I had plenty of time to get to Momeïk—where I come every week when the plane arrives—because of the post, you understand— well, I was driving slowly along the track when I heard in the distance something that sounded like a burst of gunfire. I went to see. Oh, it was curiosity rather than courage. Apart from mahjong, there's not much in the way of diversion in this country, you know.

'Anyway, I forged ahead as quickly as I could, but with these tracks and the jungle it took me some time to locate the spot. It was a defile between a high growth of thick bushes. And there, lying practically side by side, were three wounded men. Two were in police uniform and the other looked like a typical member of the Shan tribe. He obviously belonged to a gang of dacoits . . .'

'This is why there were those patrols on the road,' said Julius. 'But when I go back to Mogok they won't be there any longer. Nice and cool!'

The first passengers were lifting up their longis to their knees and beginning to get into the Dakota. The missionary went on with his tale.

'The encounter had happened by accident. The two gangs came out into the defile at the same time, each from a different side. The guns went off of their own accord. And after that the whole gallant company disappeared, leaving the wounded in the jungle.

'The police fellows were by far the most seriously hurt. One of them had got a bullet in his stomach, and it was impossible to carry him except lying down. I put him in the back of the jeep. The second one was spitting blood, but he managed to slump down in the front seat.

'As for the dacoit, he'd only got a broken leg, and so he could wait. Only he was quaking with fear for if we were going to abandon him in the wilds of the jungle where nobody would go by for days on end. The sun—thirst—wild animals who came out at night—and so on. I had to swear at least ten times that I would come back and find him. And in return, in order to make certain that I did come back, he promised to give the authorities the fullest information about the gang and its leader.'

'And who was it?' asked Jean.

The missionary didn't seem to have heard him.

'As I was starting up the truck,' he went on, 'the dacoit shouted at me again that he would also give information about the spoils his gang had collected, and which consisted of the finest rubies in the world.'

'The finest rubies——' whispered Jean.

I could see in his eyes that we both had the same curious presentiment.

The missionary shrugged his shoulders, making the flowers on his shirt ripple over his large muscles.

'Have you ever heard any important story in the Mogok area which isn't about rubies?' he asked.

'Go on! Go on!' cried Jean.

The missionary took the misshapen butt of his cigar out of his mouth, looked at it thoughtfully, threw it away, and took out a new cigar, biting the end off with a vigorous movement of the jaw.

'You've got time for the plane,' he said. 'The mail-bags are still under the wings. And it's now that the real story begins.'

Without touching his cigar he rolled it from one corner of his mouth to the other, and went on:

'So here was I setting out with my two patients, over tracks, footpaths and through brush, to the village I'd come from, where the chief of police lived, as well as the Rangoon delegate for the region.

'The two wounded men didn't speak a word, for the good reason that the one lying down was already giving the death-rattle, and the other one had fainted. Happily, I'd got my little whisky flask—by the way, you wouldn't like a nip, would you? Oh, well, you're quite right. Not before sundown—except, of course, in exceptional cases. And this was one—more so than you'd think.'

'Padre,' said Julius, 'they're loading the mail.'

'What a country!' groaned the missionary. 'You don't even have leisure to tell a story properly.'

And in his drawling, sing-song, Southern accent, which was in sharp and acutely irritating contrast to the drama of his tale, he resumed.

'Well, there I was in the village, in front of the police station. The chief of police emerged with great dignity—he was a little man, but very energetic and upright, wearing an important-looking tunic. He examined my two wounded men. The one who had the bullet in his stomach was dead. The other, whom they carried out of the jeep, was still breathing. I described to the chief of police how I'd found them in the jungle, and told him that I was going back for the dacoit. He agreed, but just at that moment the wounded man, who'd now been brought round from his faint, rapidly whispered something which I couldn't distinguish. The chief of police suddenly decided to go and get the wounded man himself. He had a jeep, too.

'I didn't reply. After all, it was his job. The wounded man wouldn't be left to the wild animals, and he could give his information straight to the right source.

'That was fine. The chief of police sneaked off on his own. I went along to see the government officer from Rangoon, and told him all about my adventure. Then we played mahjong, while we waited for the chief of police to come back with his prisoner.

'He did indeed come back at the appointed time, but just as he'd gone—alone. The dacoit, said he, proudly, seeing him approach, had tried to fire on him, and he had escaped death only because, with rapidity and justice, he had at once dispatched the bandit.'

'In that case,' said Jean, in a strained voice, 'what about his disclosures—the ruby—the end——'

'That's just what I was thinking,' said the missionary. 'And I drew the government officer's attention to it as soon as I was left with him without a witness. I also pointed out to him that the dacoit's only fear had been of perishing alone in the jungle. And that he'd known perfectly well that if I had come back, which he begged me to do, it would have been in order to hand him over to the police.

'The officer, who was the real boss, thought it all over for a bit. Then he got me to drive him, without saying a word to anyone, to the place where the skirmish had taken place. And there, after searching about in the undergrowth for a while, we found the body of the dacoit. But it was in two pieces—the head on one side and the body on the other. He hadn't been killed by a bullet. The chief of police had cut off his head with his *dah*.

'It was beginning to get dark. The animals were coming out of their lairs. If we hadn't come so soon, there wouldn't have been a single trace of that very summary execution.

'The officer picked up the severed head. He examined it thoroughly in the last rays of sunshine, and then he recognized the bandit. He was the chief of police's cousin.'

The coolies had finished loading the mail into the Dakota.

The pilot was climbing aboard. Even so, the missionary, aware that he was keeping us in suspense, couldn't resist pausing for a moment.

'And what happened then?' cried Jean and I at the same moment.

His cigar moved of its own accord from one side to the other.

'Well,' said he, 'we got back to the village, and the officer immediately collected all the soldiers at his disposal and took them to the chief of police's house. It was then that he found the treasure in the safe—and a real treasure it was.'

'Did you see it?' cried Jean.

'I tell you,' said the missionary, 'my eyes are still dazzled. What sapphires! But even more—what rubies! The chief of police was the head of the dacoits. He was holding nearly all the precious stones that had been stolen in Mogok during the last two or three years.'

'Nice and cool!' said Julius.

But Jean wasn't listening.

'All the stones that had disappeared!' he cried. 'Well then, tell me, were those of——?'

He had no chance to finish. His voice was drowned by the roar of the engines, already starting up. The propellers were turning. We had barely time to receive the last little bows from the Chinese broker and his khaki sun-helmet—barely time to take our farewells of our friend Julius, who had to go back through the jungle.

Our bags were thrown against our legs. The gangway was drawn up. The door banged shut. The aeroplane took off.

* * *

At first my mind ranged solely over the missionary's tale of murder, duplicity and blood-coloured stones. Then a multitude of questions assailed me.

Was U Min Paw's treasure among the stones recovered from this chief of police who had been in league with the dacoits? Was it he who had started to dispose of them on the Siamese market? If the Tibetan had vanished without trace was this because he had learned from some mysterious source—in the

197

opium den or elsewhere—that the hunt for the treasure was at an end? And why did all our friends in Mogok and Tchaïpin refuse to answer, or change the subject whenever we spoke of U Min Paw's jewels? Did they know, or guess, that the chief of police was in collusion with the bandits, and was this the cause of their embarrassment and fear? Even Julius himself— was this the khazouk of which he warned us?

For a moment I saw nothing with my mind's eye but the wax face of the former dacoit, U Min Paw, seated as I had seen him in the great pagoda. Then I saw the shaven head of the unfrocked bonze from Tibet.

I noticed then that the aeroplane had mounted higher.

As it did so, these sinister images dwindled and became less real. For, as I looked through the porthole of the Dakota, I could glimpse the deep green waves of the jungle, alternating with mountains and valleys. This was the land of Mogok and Tchaïpin—of the bayon, of the traditional, perhaps even millennial, mines which probed the bowels of the earth.

But what did I care about such jewels, however rare and valuable? I was held at that moment by a powerful feeling of nostalgia, as I remembered—and already they were just a memory—the ordinary folk enclosed within their valley.

I thought of their mildness, their gentle smiles, their friendliness and wisdom. I thought of their markets, splendid with colour. I thought of the laughter and peaceful gaiety of their lives.

I thought of Daw Pouanyine, the grandmother who had seen the last Burmese king; of the tranquil Daw Hla, the wealthy dealer who had once carried sacks of rice; of Maung Khin Maung, her son, with his carved face of old ivory; of Gopal Singh, the bearded giant with the ogre-like laugh; of Julius's old boy, the worthy and so charming U Nyo.

I thought of the many others there who lived as their ancestors had done, in the shadow of the pagodas, seeking rubies, playing mahjong, smoking the juice of the abundant poppies of their country.

I thought of the men, women and children of Mogok, of the welcome they had offered, and of my own good fortune in having lived among them and with them—thanks to Julius, and thanks also to Jean.

Instinctively I turned towards him. He looked in my direction. Perhaps he had felt my intent gaze upon him.

'It's wonderful, isn't it?' said Jean.

How right he was! Such a voyage with such a companion was wonderful indeed.